GEMSTONES

GEMSTONES

A complete color reference
for precious and semiprecious
stones of the world

KAREN HURRELL & MARY L. JOHNSON, PH.D.

METRO BOOKS
NEW YORK

GEMSTONES
© 2008 by Ivy Press Limited

This 2008 edition published by Metro Books,
by arrangement with Ivy Press.

This book was conceived, designed, and produced by

Ivy Press
The Old Candlemakers
West Street, Lewes,
East Sussex BN7 2NZ, U.K.

Creative Director Peter Bridgewater
Publisher Jason Hook
Editorial Director Caroline Earle
Art Director Clare Harris
Consultant Editor Mary L. Johnson, Ph.D.
Senior Editor Lorraine Turner
Senior Art Editor Sarah Howerd
Designer Ginny Zeal
Concept Design Alan Osbahr
Picture Research Katie Greenwood, Sarah Howerd

Metro Books
122 Fifth Avenue
New York, NY 10011

ISBN-13: 978-1-4351-0610-9
ISBN-10: 1-4351-0610-5

Printed and bound in China

1   3   5   7   9   10   8   6   4   2

CONTENTS

Introduction

Gems are beautiful, long-lasting, natural objects that—once fashioned by human hand—can be used for jewelry and other decorative purposes. They have always been a source of fascination; people everywhere and in all ages have treasured gemstones for their color and brilliance. Gems have been prized as status symbols, and many have been thought to have a magical or therapeutic influence. They exert a strange attraction even on those who do not believe in their otherworldly powers: Mineralogists, jewelers, and collectors all know the wonder of gems.

The raw materials of jewelry can be found throughout the world in a variety of geographical and environmental locales. Diamonds are crystals of pure carbon formed under intense pressure deep within the earth, and then carried to the surface by volcanic eruptions. Pearls grow in mollusks, in rivers, brackish marshes, and oceanic coral reefs. Gold is mined from stream beds, from veins in hard rocks, and from the leaching of volcanic deposits. It can even be extracted from sea water.

Many gems are associated with a particular country—Colombia for emeralds, say, or Burma (Myanmar) for rubies. There are some rare gems that are known to occur in only one or two places. This planet is not the only source of gems; peridot occurs in some meteorites, and cosmic dust contains very tiny diamonds. Moldavite and tektites are impact glasses formed from terrestrial rocks when meteorites struck earth.

BELOW *An alluvial diamond in a gravel bed. Diamonds make up only 0.0000005 percent of the gravel in these beds.*

Finding gems takes luck. Many historic gem sources were discovered by accident—as when a child brought home a shiny or transparent pebble. Modern explorers use ground-penetrating radar, airborne magnetic surveys, and other high-tech methods. However, the old-fashioned methods still work. The diamond sources of the Northwest Territories in Canada were found in the 1980s by tracking diamond-accompanying minerals backwards along the route that they had been carried by ancient glaciers.

ABOVE *Digging for diamonds 65 feet (20 meters) below the sea off the coast of Namibia.*

Shallow river-borne sources of gems are the easiest to exploit. As a result, they have been the object of "rushes," in which thousands of miners congregate, hoping for a lucky strike; these sources are usually depleted very quickly. Hard-rock sources are mined underground or in open pits. Industrial mining techniques are not economical if, as is often the case, the gemstones are fragile and erratically distributed. So, many gems are still mined by hand.

The easiest gemstone to mine with automated processes is the diamond, which is the hardest natural material in the world. Diamonds are extremely scarce even in the richest ore, so a mine may require an investment of billions just to determine whether it is economical. It is only the exceptionally high value we place on these glittering stones that makes mining them worthwhile.

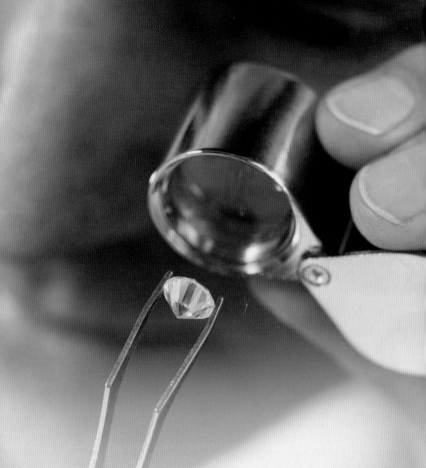

There are many ways of bringing out the beauty of a gemstone. Some methods of making gemstones more attractive, such as cleaning and the various styles of cutting, are widely

accepted. Other methods, called gemstone treatments, are more controversial. Gemstones can be oiled or coated, a process that renders fine surface cracks invisible; fractures can be filled with glass. These gemstones often need special care or can change in appearance over time. Other treatments are used to give a gemstone a prettier color; sapphires can be heat-treated for this purpose, while diamonds and topaz may be irradiated. In general, treated gems are less valuable than gems that have the same color and clarity, and have not been treated.

Some gemstones are made in the laboratory. These synthetic gems typically have natural counterparts. There are, for example, synthetic rubies, synthetic emeralds, and synthetic diamonds. If a manufactured material merely resembles a natural gem, but is different in composition, it is termed an imitation. The crystalline material known as YAG (yttrium aluminum garnet), for example, has been widely used as an imitation of diamond. Another way of making imitations is to glue two or three pieces of gem material together to make "doublets" or "triplets." Reputable jewelers will always disclose imitations, synthetics, or treated gemstones to buyers so that they can make an informed decision about what to purchase.

Gems have been used as investments from time to time, such as in the late 1970s and early 1980s. However, the value of gems is often a function of fashion, and that makes them an unpredictable investment. Moreover, their worth encourages exploration, and a big new find can turn a rare and expensive gem into one that is broadly available and affordable. This happened to the amethyst in the eighteenth century, when extensive deposits were found in Brazil and Uruguay. In the nineteenth century, when large diamond deposits were discovered in South Africa, the DeBeers consortium was formed specifically in order to prevent this new source from ruining the value of diamonds.

The value that we ascribe to gemstones has social and economic consequences. Gems, being small as well as precious, are an easily portable form of wealth, and so smuggling them is a good way to evade international financial controls. One instance of this involves so-called blood diamonds. These are diamonds that have been mined in countries that are in the grip of civil war. Child or slave labor has been used to do the mining, and the gems sold to finance war. In an effort to prevent such smuggling, the diamond trade has developed the Kimberley Process, a method of tracking diamond imports and exports.

BELOW *A trawler searching for diamonds on the ocean floor, close to the African coastline.*

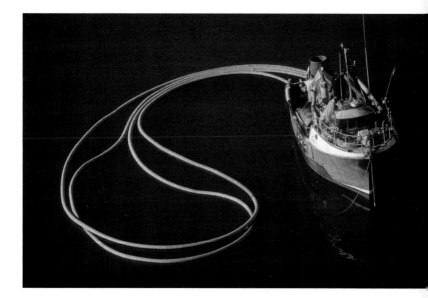

The world of gemstones

All gems are naturally occurring materials, and most of those materials are minerals. This section looks at what a mineral is, and at why only some minerals are gems. It also describes some of the other materials used in jewelry making: amber, pearls, and other organic gemstones, as well as precious metals.

Here, too, are explanations of the technical terms used to describe gems and minerals, including refractive index, dispersion, specific gravity (or density), hardness, cleavage, fracture, and luster. All these properties can be quantified scientifically, but these measurements alone are not sufficient to characterize fully a gem material. Human judgment is also involved: Among the most incisive tools to be brought to bear on a gem are a good eye and a wealth of experience.

What are minerals?

The world is made of rocks; rocks are made of minerals. There are three main kinds of solid rock. Sedimentary rocks are formed by the accumulation of small grains over time. Igneous rocks are formed from molten lava that has cooled and solidified. Metamorphic rocks are rocks that have been affected by the intense heat and pressure that prevails deep within the earth. In each case, the rock contains a mix of mineral grains, and the same mineral is found in different types of rock—just as words and sentences are made up of the same re-occurring letters.

Minerals are not the most fundamental ingredients of rocks. Each mineral is made up of atoms, and a mineral is defined by the atoms it contains, and by how those atoms are arranged. The atomic content (or chemistry) is usually described by a mineral formula, which lists the defining atoms in the mineral and gives their relative proportions. So, the formula for quartz is SiO_2, meaning that for every silicon atom (Si), there are two oxygen (O) atoms.

ABOVE *The blue-green crystals in this rock are fluorapatite, part of the apatite mineral group.*

MINERALS AND GEMSTONES
Many minerals are not suitable to be gemstones; they may be too soft or friable (crumbly), too opaque, or an unattractive color, or they may be found as too-small examples. Most gems are minerals, but some are not. Some rare, beautiful, and relatively durable organic materials are also considered gems: amber is hard, "fossilized" tree resin; coral and ivory are tough enough to be carvable; pearls (shown here) are lustrous wonders that grow in pearl oysters and other mollusks.

The world of gemstones

Minerals are defined not only by their chemical composition, but also by their "crystal structure," that is, by the way the atoms bond at a molecular level and the geometric shapes and structures that these bonds make. These structures have local order, determined by nearest- and next-nearest-neighboring atoms, and long-range order, which is determined by how the modules are stacked. The only possible stacking arrangements are those that allow the locally ordered unit cell to be repeated indefinitely in three dimensions.

Two different minerals can have the same formula (chemistry), or the same atomic arrangement (crystal structure), but they cannot have both. For example, both diamond and graphite have the same formula, C (that is, they consist of nothing but carbon atoms), but the atoms in graphite are stacked differently from those in a diamond. Minerals with the same crystal structure are sometimes said to be in the same mineral group. They do not share the same chemistry, but often have some parts of their chemistry in common.

A mineral specimen may contain small amounts of a "trace" element substituting for an element in its formula. Such traces do not make the specimen a different mineral, but it may make it a different variety. For instance, emerald is a bright green variety of the mineral beryl, and owes its green color to the presence of chromium (Cr) or vanadium (V) instead of some of the aluminum that is part of the makeup of beryl proper.

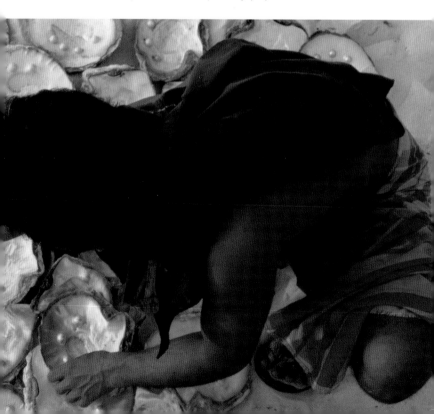

The shapes of crystals

In nature, minerals grow in a variety of ways, depending on the exact conditions under which they were formed. They may take the form of a single crystal in a clearly defined shape such as a cube, or they may form in clusters known as multiple crystal aggregates. These different manifestations of crystal growth are known as habits. Some minerals have a distinctive habit that never varies: They always grow as, say, pyramids or as six-sided columns. Other minerals have more than one habit; that is to say, the same gem may sometimes be found as a single crystal with a regular geometric shape, or else it may appear as a mass of little spiky crystals.

BLOCKY ZIRCON
CRYSTALS

MASSIVE BLUE BERYL
(AQUAMARINE)

GROUP OF BLADED
KYANITE CRYSTALS

CUBIC FLUORITE
CRYSTAL

CITRINE QUARTZ
CRYSTAL

COLUMNAR
ANDALUSITE

The number of possible mineral habits is great, and mineralogists use a large number of technical terms to describe them. Among the terms used for individual crystals are acicular (needlelike), tabular (flat, like a tile), bladed (long and flattened, like a blade of grass), blocky (boxlike, with width, length, and breadth roughly equal), and prismatic (elongated with parallel sides, like a pencil). Aggregate crystals may be botryoidal (resembling a bunch of grapes), reniform (shaped like a kidney), drusy (forming a layer of sparkling crystals), and massive (multigrained solid of no particular shape).

Whatever the habit of any given crystal, at the atomic level all crystals have limited ways for minerals to stack together to make "unit cells," the building blocks of crystals. These unit cells determine a crystal's symmetry, and symmetry is one of the biggest clues in mineral identification. All crystals can be classified into one of seven symmetry systems: cubic (or isometric), tetragonal, hexagonal, trigonal, orthorhombic, monoclinic, or triclinic.

CUBIC SYSTEM

Cubic-system unit-cells are symmetric in many different directions. Ideally, crystals may occur as cubes, octahedrons (eight-sided objects), dodecahedrons (12-sided objects), or other symmetric shapes. Among the gemstones that belong to the cubic system are diamond, spinel, and various garnets.

TETRAGONAL, HEXAGONAL, AND TRIGONAL

Tetragonal, hexagonal, and trigonal unit-cells are all symmetrical around an imaginary axis that passes through the center. Tetragonal (four-sided) crystals are symmetric to a four-fold rotation; the commonest gemstone in this group is zircon. Hexagonal crystals have a six-fold rotational axis, and the best-known example of it is beryl. Trigonal crystals have a three-fold rotation axis, and among the crystals that fall into this group are quartz, tourmaline, and corundum.

ORTHORHOMBIC, MONOCLINIC, AND TRICLINIC

The other three crystal systems—orthorhombic, monoclinic, and triclinic—do not have these rotational axes. The unit-cell of an orthorhombic crystal such as topaz is basically brick-shaped. The unit-cells for monoclinic crystals look like bricks for which one side has slid relative to the other to make a three-dimensional parallelogram: The slide means that one edge does not need to be at a right angle to the other two, but two edges are still at right angles. Examples include orthoclase (moonstone) and diopside. Triclinic crystals can be blunt or sharp wedges; examples of these include microcline and axinite.

What is a gem?

A gem is a natural material suitable for use as an ornament. It has three characteristics: It should be beautiful, durable, and rare. Beauty is not, of course, a scientific category but in the eyes of most beholders, beautiful gems are usually transparent and either colorless or vividly colored. Some gems, such as opals or well-cut diamonds, show flashes of bright color as the gem is moved. Some phenomena allow or require reduced transparency; these include cat's eyes (chatoyancy) and stars (asterism). Other gems, such as alexandrite, change color with different light sources. Some opaque gems, such as lapis lazuli, display an intensity of color that more than compensates for their lack of transparency.

Durability in a gem means that it is resistant to scratching and impact. The hardness of a mineral is measured on the Mohs scale, according to which the softest mineral (talc) is 1 and the hardest (diamond) is 10. Gems that are to be worn as jewelry should rate 7 at least—because then they cannot be scratched by the microscopic grains of quartz that are present in everyday dust. The corundum gems ruby and sapphire are durable enough to be used as watch bearings and faces, and can be scratched only by diamonds. Diamonds, as hard as they are, can be shattered or cleaved (broken in parts) by impact. The jades—jadeite and nephrite—are perhaps the toughest gems. They are not single crystals, but are made of interlocking grains. This means that they are hard to break, but at the same time amenable to being carved.

RIGHT *Olmec mask carved from jadeite jade 1200 years ago.*

The rarity of a gem can work against it commercially. If a gem is very uncommon, too few people are familiar enough with it to appreciate it. A more widely available gem

ABOVE Lustrous pearls such as these can be damaged by perfumes and even some skin oils.

material will inevitably exhibit more variations in color, clarity, size, and other qualities, allowing buyers greater choice. However, certain colors, clarities, and sizes will be rarer than others. The most common gem materials naturally tend to be the least expensive, but fine workmanship in the cutting and mounting of a gem can turn an inexpensive rough into something valuable and desirable.

No gem is impervious to every condition to which it may be exposed. Some gemstones, such as most emeralds, are brittle; others, such as tanzanite, are very prone to cleavage or breakage. Pearls are extremely soft, and can even be damaged by the oils in the skin. The popularity of these more fragile gems demonstrates that beauty is by far the most important factor when it comes to gemstones. However, durability will govern the use to which a gem is put; whether it is worn daily in a ring, brought out for special occasions only, or kept as part of a collection.

Precious metals

Precious metals are closely associated with gems and minerals—not only because they are used to make the settings for cut stones, but also because they can occur as inclusions in some gems and lend them a distinctive color. The most commonly used precious metals are gold, silver, and platinum.

Gold is almost indestructible, and is a good medium for jewelry since it never tarnishes. It forms in igneous rocks and associated quartz veins, as well as in placer deposits. It cannot be used in its pure form because it is too soft, so it is often alloyed with other metals such as silver and copper. The purity of gold is expressed in carats (abbreviated to "ct," or to "K" in the USA and some other countries). Pure gold is said to be 24 carats. An alloy that is 92 percent gold is 22 carat; 75 percent gold is 18 carat; 37.5 percent gold is 9 carat.

Unlike gold, silver usually occurs in combination with other elements. Much silver is produced from silver-bearing minerals such as prousite, pyrargyrite, and galena. Silver metal in its pure state has a brilliant white metallic luster. It is a little harder than gold, but very malleable. Archaeological remains tell us that humankind learned to separate silver from lead as early as 3000 BCE. From that time until now, silver has been used for jewelry and for coinage. Jewelry and silverware are traditionally made from sterling silver, an alloy consisting of 92.5 percent silver and 7.5 percent copper. Sterling silver is harder than pure silver and has a lower melting point. An alternative standard, called Britannia silver and containing a silver content of 95.8 percent, is used to make tableware and wrought plate.

BELOW *Precious metals occur as crystals, in chemical compounds, or in nugget form—like this gold.*

Platinum is a relative newcomer to the scene. It was not recognized as an element until the eighteenth century. It is like gold in that it does not tarnish, but it is heavier and far more rare. In appearance it resembles silver, but it can also have a white or greyish hue. Pure platinum is unknown in nature, and it is usually alloyed with other metals such as iron, copper, gold, nickel, iridium, palladium, rhodium, ruthenium, and osmium. Well-formed crystals of platinum are very rare, and when they do occur they have a distinctive cubic structure, like little metal dice. Platinum is more likely to be found in the form of nuggets and grains. It usually occurs in ore as a minor element in pentlandite, and exists in two rare minerals: sperrylite and cooperite. It was only in the 1920s that the technology was developed to melt platinum reliably (its melting point is 3,223°F, 1,773°C). Consequently, most platinum settings have a very modern appearance which, combined with the monetary value of this beautiful metal, makes platinum jewelry a highly prized and extremely desirable commodity.

ABOVE *Many pieces of jewelry, like these bangles and toe rings, consist of metal only and contain no gemstones.*

SILVER

GOLD

PLATINUM

The language of gemstones

Gems are defined and identified according to various characteristics, which are listed for each of the gems in the following directory. These are some of the essential properties and categories that are used by mineralogists to classify gemstones.

Class: The chemical composition and structure of the gem. Some groups of atoms are considered to form the "backbone" of the crystal structure. Examples include carbon-oxygen groups (carbonates), phosphorus-oxygen groups (phosphates), and several configurations of silicon-oxygen groups (such as chain silicates and cyclosilicates).

Amethyst—class: silicates.

Crystal system: The basic symmetry of a mineral at the atomic scale, which dictates how it grows. There are seven crystal systems: isometric (or cubic), tetragonal, hexagonal, trigonal, orthorhombic, monoclinic, and triclinic (see also page 15). A material that is disorganized at the atomic scale, such as natural glass, is termed amorphous. Some gem materials do not have order on the atomic scale, but are organized on larger scales; these include opals, and also organic structures such as shells and pearls.

Pyrite—crystal system: cubic; composition: iron sulfide.

Composition: The atomic content (chemistry), usually described by a mineral formula listing the defining atoms in the mineral and their relative proportions.

Refractive index: The atoms in a crystal slow down light, compared to its speed in a vacuum. The refractive index measures this slowing. Since atoms can be more closely packed in some directions than in others, slowing the light more in the denser directions, some minerals have two or even three refractive indices.

Ruby—refractive index: 1.761–1.769.

Birefringence: The difference between the highest and lowest refractive index in a mineral that has more than one refractive index value.

Chrysoprase—birefringence: up to 0.004.

Dispersion: Each color of the spectrum has its own associated wavelength. The refractive index of a material is different at different wavelengths (so the proper refractive index is measured at 589 nm, in the yellow region of the spectrum). Dispersion measures the difference in refractive index (for light traveling in the same direction) between blue-violet light (at 486 nm) and red light (at 656 nm).

Purple fluorite—dispersion 0.007.

Specific gravity: Specific gravity measures how much an object weighs relative to the same volume of water. A gem with a high specific gravity, such as white jadeite, will feel heavier in the hand than one with a low specific gravity, such as white opal.

Opal—specific gravity: 1.98–2.20.

Hardness: This is the resistance of a material to scratching. A harder mineral scratches a softer mineral. Hardness is measured using the Mohs Scale, according to which talc has a hardness of 1, gypsum 2, calcite 3, fluorite 4, apatite 5, orthoclase 6, quartz 7, topaz 8, corundum 9, and diamond 10.

Diamond—hardness: 10.

Cleavage: This is the natural tendency of a mineral to break along flat planes. These breakage surfaces correspond to planes where the bonding between atoms is weak.

Fracture: This is the way a mineral breaks along lines other than a flat cleavage plane. A fracture may be described as, for example, conchoidal (curved, or "shell-like"), hackly (jagged), splintery, or uneven.

Malachite—cleavage: perfect in one direction, fair in another.

Luster: This is the way that a mineral reflects light. Transparent minerals can have a luster that is adamantine (diamond-like), vitreous (glassy), resinous (like amber or plastic), silky, dull, earthy, or pearly. Opaque minerals may also have metallic or submetallic (almost metallic) luster.

Habit: This refers to the common way a mineral grows, such as in cubes, kidney-like masses, and so on (see also page 14).

Pearl—fracture: uneven; luster: pearly; habit: round to baroque shapes.

The language of gemstones

The gemstone directory

This directory showcases 130 of the world's most beautiful gems and gem minerals, natural glasses, and organic gems. Each one is shown in both its natural state and its cut form. The characteristics and uses of every gem are described, and each entry has an easy-reference section that gives all the gem's technical properties.

Gem minerals may be found as well-formed or roughly formed crystals, broken pieces, or waterworn nodules, all of which can be fashioned into gems. Natural glass—such as obsidian—is formed when molten rock cools too rapidly for crystals to form. Organic gems include coral, which is the fossilized remains of tiny marine creatures, and pearls and shells, which are derived from hard living tissue that grows in much the same way as bones and teeth.

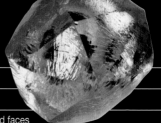

Class: native elements

Crystal system: cubic

Composition: carbon

Habit: octahedra, cubes, etc., often with curved faces

The name diamond is derived from the Greek *adamas*, meaning "inconquerable," a reference to its hardness. Diamonds are the hardest minerals on earth, and because of their luster, high refractive power, rarity, and resilience, they are the most precious of all gemstones.

Properties and characteristics: Diamonds can be colorless, or may appear in a range of hues, including yellow, brown, blue, pink, green, and red. They are transparent to translucent, with some specimens being opaque. These qualities are dependent on the type and number of inclusions, with graphite being the most common inclusion. Diamonds are formed in high-pressure environments in the earth's lower crust and mantle, and transported to the surface by igneous kimberlite pipes. Because of their durability, they are often recovered from placer deposits. Diamonds can be treated in a number of ways to change their appearance. Heat, pressure-treatment, and/or irradiation may be used to encourage a certain tint or coloration, or to make a diamond colorless. Synthetic diamonds have been produced since the 1950s.

Cutting, setting, and valuing: Many diamonds used as gems contain inclusions, fissures, and other clarity characteristics. A grading system has been set up to evaluate diamonds based on their clarity as well as their color, cut, and carat weight. The most popular diamonds are colorless, although most have a tint (often yellow or brown) that is not always evident to the untrained eye. Bright yellow diamonds have recently become more popular. Clear diamonds are much more valuable than yellowish, brownish, or grayish stones, but intensely colored "fancies" command high prices. Diamonds are cut as brilliant, square radiant, and princess cuts, cushions, pears, hearts, marquises, and briolettes; the brilliant cut is often used for ring centerstones.

Refractive index:	2.42
Birefringence:	none
Dispersion:	0.044
Specific gravity:	3.52
Hardness:	10
Cleavage:	perfect in four directions
Fracture:	conchoidal
Luster:	adamantine to greasy
Notable locations:	South Africa, Botswana, Namibia, and many other African countries, India, Brazil, Venezuela, Russia, Australia, Indonesia, Canada, Arkansas in the USA
Color:	pale yellows, browns, grays, and also white, blue, black, pink, red, purple, orange, green, and colorless

Cubic Diamond

Pyrope
Garnet

Class: silicates (silicates with isolated silica units)

Crystal system: cubic

Composition: magnesium aluminum silicate

Habit: dodecahedral or trapezohedral crystals

The name pyrope comes from the Greek word meaning "firelike," and this variety of garnet is typically red. Pyrope is less common than most garnets, but it is widely used as a gemstone. Pyrope is difficult to distinguish from almandine without a spectroscope, but it usually displays fewer flaws and inclusions. High-chromium varieties from volcanic pipes (such as diamond pipes) are known as chrome pyrope.

Properties and characteristics: Nearly all pyrope comes from ultramafic igneous rocks, which also contain olivine and/or diamond. Metamorphic pyrope occurs when these igneous rocks are metamorphosed, and also from rocks that are rich in magnesium. Almandine and pyrope comprise a series in which iron replaces the magnesium in pyrope. In fact, pure pyrope is very rare in nature and the various proportions of the two minerals are known as pyrope-almandine mixes. One intermediate stone between the two is the variety called rhodolite, which is a rich red-purple colored stone. A rare intermediate between pyrope, almandite, and spessartine is a color-change garnet from Madagascar, which is blue in some lighting.

Cutting, setting, and valuing: Red pyrope is very dark in tone, or occurs in small sizes (so-called "ant hill garnets"). Because of this, gems are rarely faceted (as mixed or brilliant cuts) in sizes over one carat. Stones over two to three carats are the most valuable. American and South African pyropes are lighter than those from Bohemia; lighter, brighter stones are more expensive than darker stones, with pale pinks and reds, and brighter reds, purples, and pinks commanding the highest prices. The very light pink pyropes from the Dora Massif are often shattered and so rarely occur as large stones.

Refractive index:	1.715–1.75
Birefringence:	none
Dispersion:	0.022
Specific gravity:	3.51–3.80
Hardness:	7–7.5
Cleavage:	none
Fracture:	conchoidal
Luster:	greasy to vitreous
Notable locations:	Bohemia in the Czech Republic, the Dora-Maira Massif in Italy, other localities in Europe, Arizona in the USA, South Africa, Australia, Tanzania, Brazil
Color:	shades of red, sometimes colorless to pink for very pure examples

Cubic Pyrope

Spessartine
Garnet

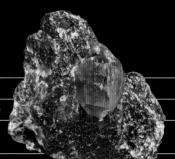

Class: silicates (silicates with isolated silica units)

Crystal system: cubic

Composition: manganese aluminum silicate

Habit: dodecahedral or trapezohedral crystals

This garnet is named after Spessart Forest in Bavaria, Germany, where it was first found. Until a discovery in the early 1990s of bright orange stones in Namibia (where the stone became known as mandarin garnet), spessartine was infrequently seen in jewelry. Demand for it is, however, growing because of the gem's excellent hardness and brilliance, which is the result of its very high refractive index.

Properties and characteristics: Like other garnets, spessartine inevitably occurs in a blend with other species. Gems with the highest spessartine content are soft orange in color, while those that contain more almandine are reddish to red brown. Manganese is the main element that gives spessartine its orange color. An increased iron content makes the stone darker and/or reddish. Inclusions can appear feathery or lacelike. Spessartine can be found in both metamorphic and igneous rock.

Cutting, setting, and valuing: Spessartine is less common than most other garnets, and does not usually occur as transparent, gemstone-quality specimens. Rare mandarin garnet from Namibia is expensive since it is hard to come by. The other valuable spessartines are a bright, orangish red. These formerly came from Ramona, California, and Amelia Courthouse, Virginia (USA); current sources include Pakistan, Nigeria, and Brazil. Spessartine is normally cut either in facets or en cabochon.

Refractive index:	1.79–1.81
Birefringence:	none
Dispersion:	0.027
Specific gravity:	4.12–4.20
Hardness:	7–7.5
Cleavage:	none
Fracture:	subconchoidal
Luster:	vitreous
Notable locations:	Pakistan, Australia, Sri Lanka, USA, Sweden, Burma (Myanmar), Brazil, Namibia, China, Nigeria
Color:	red, reddish orange, bright orange, yellowish brown, reddish brown, brown

Cubic Spessartine

Almandine
Garnet

Class: silicates (silicates with isolated silica units)

Crystal system: cubic

Composition: iron aluminum silicate

Habit: dodecahedral or trapezohedral crystals

Almandine is the most common garnet, and is normally found in garnet schists (a type of metamorphic rock that occurs in flat layers and consists primarily of mica). Garnets displaying a reflection of light in the shape of a star (asterism) are not common. The name almandine has evolved from the name of a Turkish city called Alabanda.

Properties and characteristics: Pure almandine and pure pyrope are rare, and most specimens are intermediate between the two. They can be told apart by their density (almandine has a specific gravity of about 4.3 while pyrope has a specific gravity nearer to 3.6). The depth of its color varies enormously, depending upon the level of iron; magnesium can substitute for iron, making the stone more like pyrope. Although almandine has a brilliant luster, even clear stones have limited transparency because their color is so deep.

Cutting, setting, and valuing: Because almandines are so common (they are found worldwide), their value is low. Large crystals do exist, but because of their dark tone, only small to medium-sized gems are faceted. These stones are cut shallowly to allow the light to pass through. Almandine garnets from Idaho and India with rutile inclusions sometimes produce stones with an asterism when properly cut; these are highly prized by collectors. Darker almandines are often cut as cabochons, with the bottom of the stone hollowed out to encourage more light to filter through. Rose cuts have also been used, particularly in the past. Nowadays, when the material is quite transparent, faceted cuts are used as well, and sometimes square or rectangular step cuts. Gems of several carats are not uncommon.

Refractive index:	1.78–1.83
Birefringence:	none
Dispersion:	0.027
Specific gravity:	3.95–4.25
Hardness:	7–7.5
Cleavage:	none
Fracture:	conchoidal
Luster:	vitreous
Notable locations:	Alaska in the USA, Germany, Norway, India
Color:	red to brown, sometimes purplish, and deep black-red

Cubic Almandine

Uvarovite
Garnet

Class: silicates (silicates with isolated silica units)

Crystal system: cubic

Composition: calcium chromium silicate

Habit: dodecahedral or trapezohedral
crystals

Uvarovite is a green-colored garnet that occurs as druses of tiny crystals. It is named after a Russian noble, Count Sergei Uvarov (1765–1855), who was president of the St. Petersburg Academy and a mineral collector. This gemstone is among the rarest of the garnet species. The characteristic rich, dark green color is the result of chromium in its composition. The Ural Mountains of Russia remain the best source of uvarovite, and although good secondary sources include Finland, South Africa, and California, Russia produces the finest, most beautiful gems. Finnish gems often appear as large individuals or crystal clusters, and are sought after by collectors. The best Finnish gems are found in a copper mine in Outokumpu.

Properties and characteristics: The crystals are usually opaque, and high-quality crystals resemble the best emeralds. Mineral specimens of uvarovite are prized by collectors because of their spectacular color and brilliance. One of the calcium-rich members of the garnet group, uvarovite forms when certain limestones that are rich in silica metamorphose. It is often found alongside chromite and serpentine. Uvarovite also occurs in the bright green Burmese rock maw-sit-sit. Chromian grossular, tsavorite, and demantoid (andradite) are sometimes mistaken for (or misrepresented as) uvarovite.

Cutting, setting, and valuing: This exquisite green mineral occurs as small, opaque crystals that occasionally have a transparent portion that is large enough for cutting a faceted gem. Many contemporary trade shows offer the crusts of small crystals on matrix, which has produced a new interest in the stone. Many modern designers are using the drusy material for unusual jewelry. A faceted uvarovite over one carat is extremely rare.

Birefringence:	none
Dispersion:	not applicable
Specific gravity:	3.77
Hardness:	7.5
Cleavage:	none
Fracture:	conchoidal
Luster:	vitreous
Notable locations:	Russia, California, South Africa, Finland, Burma (Myanmar)
Color:	green

Cubic Uvarovite

Grossular
Garnet

Class: silicates (silicates with isolated silica units)

Crystal system: cubic

Composition: calcium aluminum silicate

Habit: dodecahedral or trapezohedral crystals,
often showing growth zoning

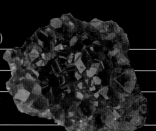

This garnet acquired its name from the word grossularia. This is the botanical name for gooseberry, which shares a similar light yellow-green color with the first grossular garnets. Unlike the most other garnets, grossulars are rarely red or dark in color.

Properties and characteristics: Small amounts of the elements iron, manganese, chromium, vanadium, and titanium produce various shades of yellow, brown, green, orange-brown, raspberry red, and pink. Grossulars lacking these are colorless or white. Round or ovoid inclusions are common in some varieties of grossular garnets. The name hessonite has been given to a type of deep yellow to brown grossular garnet. Tsavorite, or tsavolite, is a green grossular that owes its color to its vanadium composition. Other grossular garnets include colorless leucogarnet and bright pink "raspberry garnet." There are even hydrous relatives of grossular garnets that occur in massive form resembling jade and are known as "watermelon garnet" or "Transvaal jade" (not a real jade).

Cutting, setting, and valuing: The orange variety is the most common and specimens of orange grossular crystals are prized by many collectors. Colorless grossularite is the least common. Grossular garnets are generally faceted, but some are cut as beads.

Refractive index:	1.739–1.748
Birefringence:	none
Dispersion:	0.027
Specific gravity:	3.57–3.65
Hardness:	7–7.5
Cleavage:	none
Fracture:	subconchoidal
Luster:	vitreous to resinous
Notable locations:	Asbestos, Quebec, Canada, Mexico, Kenya, Italy, Pakistan, Russia, Sri Lanka
Color:	colorless, yellow, orange, green, red, pink, cinnamon brown

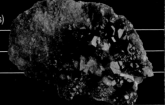

The name hessonite comes from the Greek *hesson*, meaning "inferior," which alludes to the fact that the stone was believed to have a lower hardness and density than most other garnets. Its characteristic color is similar to that of zircon, with which it has often been confused. One difference is the specific gravity (hessonite being about 3.65 and zircon coming in around 4.6 to 4.8). A grossular garnet, hessonite is also known as "cinnamon stone" because of its spicy color.

Properties and characteristics: Minor amounts of both iron and manganese are found in hessonite. Differences in the amounts account for the variations in color from a rich reddish brown to orange, pinkish orange, and pale honey-yellow. The highest-quality hessonite garnets come from Sri Lanka, where they appear in metamorphic rocks, gem gravels, and sands. Hessonite's appearance is considered to be "treacly" or like "scotch and water," as a result of its swirls of inclusions. Hessonite may usually be recognized, even when cut, by its unusually grainy structure. This makes the stone appear as if it was composed of tiny grains glued together.

Cutting, setting, and valuing: Although hessonite is not uncommon, it is not often seen on the market. At one time, hessonite was in considerable demand, but it is too brownish and too imperfectly transparent to be popular today. Only the yellow and orange shades of hessonite are used for jewelry. In the past, cutting was almost invariably rounded or en cabochon, but by the middle of the twentieth century, the brilliant-cut front and the step-cut back was commonly adopted.

Refractive index:	1.742–1.748
Birefringence:	none
Dispersion:	0.027
Specific gravity:	about 3.65
Hardness:	7–7.5
Cleavage:	none
Fracture:	conchoidal to uneven
Luster:	vitreous to resinous
Notable locations:	Sri Lanka, Brazil, California
Color:	red, brown, orange, gold

Cubic Hessonite

Tsavorite
Grossular Garnet

Class: silicates (silicates with isolated silica units)

Crystal system: cubic

Composition: calcium aluminum silicate

Habit: dodecahedral or trapezohedral crystals

Tsavorite is named after the Tsavo National Park, near the border between Kenya and Tanzania, where it was first found. It is the vanadium-colored green variety of grossularite. Most tsavorite deposits are small and irregular, and the material often occurs in "pods."

Properties and characteristics: This grossular garnet occurs in the Mozambique belt, which is a geological formation that consists of high-grade metamorphic rocks, and stretches three thousand miles (almost five thousand kilometers) up the east coast of Africa from Mozambique in the south-southeast through the countries of Tanzania, Kenya, Ethiopia, and Sudan. The rocks of the Mozambique belt are a mix of volcanic rocks, ancient (precambrian) sediments, and intrusions that have undergone several metamorphic phases which have altered the initial character of the rocks.

Cutting, setting, and valuing: These popular gems command high prices in the current market. Most faceted stones are less than three carats because of their dark coloration, but there are faceted stones of up to 15 carats. Gemstones under one carat are normally found. Tsavorite is popular for its unusual and beautiful color. Slightly bluish green stones tend to be the most coveted, and those that appear yellowish are in less demand. Emerald cuts are popular. However, because tsavorite has a higher refractive index than emeralds, and more than double the dispersion, the brilliant cut is better used to provide even greater brilliance. Tsavorite is rare, and therefore expensive.

Refractive index:	1.739–1.744
Birefringence:	none
Dispersion:	0.027
Specific gravity:	3.57–3.65
Hardness:	7–7.5
Cleavage:	none
Fracture:	conchoidal to uneven
Luster:	vitreous
Notable locations:	Kenya, Tanzania
Color:	light to deep or bluish green

Cubic Tsavorite

Andradite
Garnet

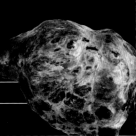

Class: silicate (silicates with isolated silica units)

Crystal system: cubic

Composition: calcium iron silicate

Habit: dodecahedral or trapezohedral crystals, often
showing growth zoning

**Andradite was named to honor the Portuguese mineralogist, Jose
Bonifacio de Andrada e Silva (1763–1838). This is one of the most sought-
after garnets. Supply is restricted to fairly small deposits. Andradite
garnet contains calcium and iron. Yellow andradite is called topazolite,
and vibrant green andradite is known in the trade as demantoid. Melanite
is a black (occasionally dark red), titanium-rich variety of andradite
garnet. Brown andradite, the commonest color, is rarely faceted or used
in jewelry. A few andradites are found with an iridescent sheen on some
faces; these stones come from Mexico and Japan.**

Properties and characteristics: Andradite's dispersion is much higher
than that of any other garnet and significantly higher than that of a diamond.
Dark body colors normally mask the dispersion, but small, pale, and well-cut
gems are impressively fiery. Demantoid is the most valuable of the andradite
garnets. The finest material is found in alluvial goldbearing deposits in the Ural
Mountains in Russia, and also in metamorphic formations, but other good
sources are located in Namibia and Iran. Demantoid's color can vary from a
very pale green to a rich, medium green colored by chromium. Material from
Russia (and other sources) have characteristic "horsetail" inclusions.

Cutting, setting, and valuing: Some transparent green andradite is described
as demantoid, or diamond-like, because of its high dispersion. Faceted
demantoid gems over two carats are extremely rare. The gemstone qualities
of topazolite garnets are a good match for demantoids, but because they are
very small, they are not practical for jewelry use. It is rare to find faceted gems
larger than two or three carats.

Refractive index:	1.888–1.889 (green)
Birefringence:	none
Dispersion:	0.057
Specific gravity:	3.82–3.85 (green)
Hardness:	6.5
Cleavage:	none
Fracture:	conchoidal
Luster:	vitreous to adamantine
Notable locations:	Italy, Mexico, Japan, Ural Mountains in Russia, California and Arizona in the USA
Color:	bright green, black, yellowish brown, red, greenish yellow, gray

Pyrite

Class: sulfides

Crystal system: cubic

Composition: iron sulfide

Habit: cubes, pentagonal dodecahedra, octahedra, etc.

The name pyrite derives from the Greek words *pyrites lithos*, meaning "stone which strikes fire." This alludes to the sparking that is produced when pyrite is struck by steel. Pyrite is also known as "fool's gold" because of its color. Pyrite is a common mineral and has a high iron content. However, it has never been used as a noteworthy source of iron, although it has been mined for its sulfur content. Pyrite is often confused with marcasite, which has the same chemical composition but a different crystal structure.

Properties and characteristics: Pyrite is the most widespread and plentiful sulfide mineral in all types of rocks and is, in fact, found in almost every possible environment. Pyrite is frequently associated with many different metal ores, and it forms concretionary masses in sedimentary rocks. It is common, too, in coal, slates, and other metamorphic rocks. It has a greenish black streak, conducts electricity, and generates a weak electric current when heated. It is pyrite's isometric crystals that distinguish it from the chemically identical marcasite, which has orthorhombic crystals.

Cutting, setting, and valuing: Because of its abundance in nature, pyrite has almost no intrinsic value except in large quantities, in which case it forms an ore of sulfur. However, as is true for all minerals, spectacularly aesthetic specimens are quite valuable. When cut into ornamental objects, it is attractive; in the past, it has been in favor, and used in bracelets, brooches, scarf and tie pins, and, in some cases, rings. Cabochon and polished stones are the most common cuts for modern ornamental use. Pyrite has also been faceted to show off the brilliant luster; these are usually small accent stones, marketed as marcasites.

Refractive index:	opaque
Birefringence:	none
Dispersion:	none
Specific gravity:	4.85–4.90
Hardness:	6–6.5
Cleavage:	indistinct
Fracture:	uneven, sometimes conchoidal
Luster:	metallic
Notable locations:	Illinois and Missouri in the USA, Peru, Spain
Color:	pale brass yellow

Cubic Pyrite

Sphalerite

Class: sulfides

Crystal system: cubic

Composition: zinc sulfide

Habit: tetrahedra, dodecahedra, banded massive

Sphalerite is a soft, brittle mineral, also known as blende, which can occur in a wide range of colors, most commonly in reddish, orange, yellow, and brownish hues. The name sphalerite has been derived from Greek word for "treacherous" and blende from the German for "blind" or "deceiving," since it resembles galena but contains no lead. The iron content in this mineral increases the darker shade, and opaque metallic crystals are known as marmatite. It is often difficult to differentiate between sphalerite and other valuable ore minerals such as galena, acanthite, and tetrahedrite.

Properties and characteristics: Dark specimens of sphalerite can appear fairly metallic in luster, but the luster is generally described as being resinous or adamantine. Sphalerite usually occurs as tetrahedral crystals or dodecahedra, and can occur in granular or massive form. Its noteworthy dodecahedral cleavage allows it to be chipped into beautiful 12-sided pieces, with careful cutting. Some specimens fluoresce orange in ultraviolet light, and may also display triboluminescence, producing orange flashes when stroked with a knife. When gently rubbed, a piece of sphalerite smells like sulfur.

Cutting, setting, and valuing: The mineral is almost always nearly black in color but it is occasionally found in transparent pieces of orange or yellowish brown, in which case it can be cut as a collector's gem. Green, yellowish green, bluish green, and colorless sphalerite are rare. This mineral has a very high refractive index and an extremely high dispersion, which makes well-cut sphalerite gems truly brilliant. Because of its hardness (3.5–4 on the Mohs hardness scale) and the fact that it has six directions of perfect cleavage, sphalerite is unsuitable for most jewelry.

Refractive index:	2.37
Birefringence:	none
Dispersion:	0.156
Specific gravity:	4.09
Hardness:	3.5–4
Cleavage:	perfect in six directions
Fracture:	conchoidal
Luster:	metallic to resinous
Notable locations:	Spain, Bulgaria, Mexico, Italy, Peru, China; also Joplin in Missouri, Rosiclare in Illinois, Elmwood in Tennessee, USA; Broken Hill in Australia
Color:	yellow, orange, red, green, brown, black

Cubic Sphalerite

Spinel

Class:	oxides and hydroxides
Crystal system:	cubic
Composition:	magnesium aluminum oxide
Habit:	octahedra or triangular "macle" twins

Spinel's typical red color rivals that of ruby. In fact, many famous rubies were found to be spinels. The two stones are chemically similar, with spinel being composed of magnesium aluminum oxide, and ruby aluminum oxide. Spinel was first recognized as a separate gem in Burma in 1587. Spinel's name is derived from the Italian word *spinella* ("little thorn"), from the Latin word for "thorn" (*spina*), which alludes to the fact that its characteristic octahedral crystals have pointed ends.

Properties and characteristics: The name spinel also refers to a group of related minerals, including spinel itself, gahnite, hercynite, and others. Most colorful gem material is the mineral spinel, but dark colors may represent other species. Spinel is mined from the metamorphic rock primary deposits in which it forms, but comes mostly from alluvial or placer deposits. Spinel is an allochromatic gemstone. This means that when the mineral is pure, it is colorless; colors are derived only from the presence of minor elements. In the case of spinel, these are iron, chromium, manganese, and, in bright blue spinels, cobalt. Rutile inclusions can produce beautiful six- or four-rayed stars.

Cutting, setting, and valuing: High-quality natural spinel is a rare gem, but it has only recently attracted widespread attention. Spinels can be found in very large sizes. By far the most common colors (and therefore the least valuable) are pale to medium mauve-pink and grayish pale purple. The most highly valued spinels are red to purplish red and cobalt blue. Burmese spinels are also more expensive. Spinel's hardness makes it a good choice for almost all jewelry applications (including rings) and it is normally cut as a brilliant, cushion, step, mixed, or cabochon. Flame-fusion synthetic spinel is widely available, and flux synthetic spinels can be easily confused with natural gems.

Refractive index:	1.712–1.80
Birefringence:	none
Dispersion:	0.020
Specific gravity:	3.58–4.06
Hardness:	7.5–8.0
Cleavage:	none
Fracture:	conchoidal
Luster:	vitreous
Notable locations:	Burma (Myanmar), Sri Lanka, Brazil, Vietnam, Afghanistan
Color:	mainly red, but also pink, colorless, blue, purple, green, brown, and black

Cubic Spinel

Fluorite

Class: halides

Crystal system: cubic

Composition: calcium fluoride

Habit: cubes and octahedrons are the commonest of many habits

Fluorite is soft, easily scratched, and has a perfect cleavage in four directions, which makes it largely unsuitable for jewelry. It is, however, a collector's gem, and a well-cut and polished gem can be both bright and attractive. Once called fluorspar by miners, fluorite has been used in carvings and decorative objects for centuries. Only recently has this stone been faceted for a larger market. The name, from the Latin *fluere* ("to flow"), refers to the fact that it melts easily, a property that makes it a useful flux in industrial steel production.

Properties and characteristics: The huge variety of fluorite colors, which include purple, blue, green, yellow, colorless, brown, pink, black, and reddish orange, is exceptional; only quartz has as many variations. Most specimens contain a single color, but some have multiple colors, often arranged in bands and zones that reflect the crystal shapes. Fluorite is frequently fluorescent under longwave ultraviolet light, and its fluorescent colors can vary considerably. Typically it fluoresces blue-to-violet but other fluorescent colors include green, white, and brown.

Cutting, setting, and valuing: The colorless variety is less popular than colored varieties. Rare colors of pink, reddish orange, and black are in demand. Purple is the most common and, surprisingly, popular color. Cushion, step, and mixed are the most frequently used cuts, although cameos have been made. Multicolored faceted stones are also fashionable. Some natural pink stones fade quickly in sunlight. Synthetic fluorite exists, but is rare.

Refractive index:	1.43
Birefringence:	none
Dispersion:	0.007
Specific gravity:	3.18
Hardness:	4
Cleavage:	perfect in four directions
Fracture:	irregular and brittle
Luster:	vitreous
Notable locations:	Switzerland, USA, Mexico, England, China, Argentina, Namibia
Color:	purple, blue, green or yellow; also colorless, reddish orange, pink, white, and brown (a single crystal can be multicolored)

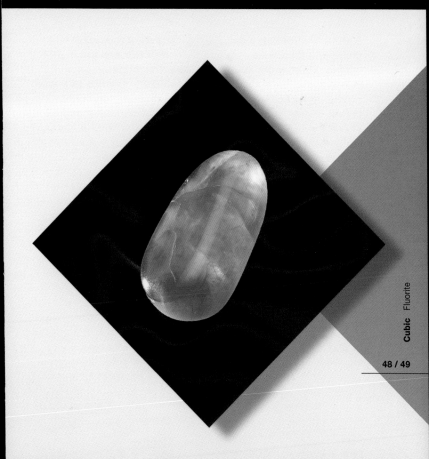

Cubic Fluorite

Sodalite

Class: silicates (framework silicates)

Crystal system: cubic

Composition: sodium aluminum silicate chloride

Habit: massive; rare dodecahedral crystals

Sodalite is a type of feldspathoid, one of a group of tectosilicate (framework silicate) minerals that resemble feldspars, but have a different structure and much lower silica content. They occur in rare and unusual types of igneous rocks. The name sodalite refers to its sodium content. It was first discovered in 1806 in Greenland; however, sodalite did not become an important decorative stone until 1891 when huge deposits of high-quality material were discovered in Bancroft, Ontario, Canada. This stone is sometimes called "Princess Blue" sodalite after Princess Patricia, who chose sodalite to decorate Marlborough House in the UK, following a visit to Ontario.

Properties and characteristics: Sodalite and lapis lazuli share an almost identical composition, except lapis lazuli contains sulfur instead of sodalite's chlorine. Well known for its violet-blue color, sodalite may also be gray, yellow, green, or pink, and can be dappled with white veins or patches. The pink variety, known as hackmanite, and found in gem quality in Burma (Myanmar) is brightly fluorescent and also reversibly sensitive to light, causing it to fade to white in daylight and then revert to magenta pink when exposed to ultraviolet light. Sodalite is usually found in syenite and trachyte rocks. Other large deposits of sodalite have been found in Brazil, specifically Bahia.

Cutting, setting, and valuing: Sodalite is celebrated in the semiprecious stone market, and is often used for carving, mineral specimens, and decorative stone. Crystals are scarce. The more homogeneously blue specimens are used in jewelry, where the material is fashioned into cabochons and beads. Well-colored faceted gems are very beautiful but tend to be inadequately transparent. Deep-blue transparent sodalite is rare and relatively expensive.

Refractive index:	1.48
Birefringence:	none
Dispersion:	0.018
Specific gravity:	2.15–2.35
Hardness:	5.5–6
Cleavage:	poor
Fracture:	uneven, conchoidal
Luster:	vitreous to greasy
Notable locations:	Canada, USA, Burma (Myanmar), Russia, Brazil, India, Bolivia
Color:	azure blue, white, pink, gray, green

Cubic Sodalite

Haüyne

Class: silicates (framework silicates)

Crystal system: cubic

Composition: complex silicate

Habit: small rounded crystals or dodecahedra

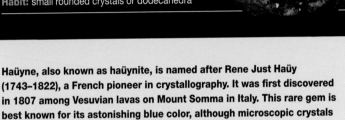

Haüyne, also known as haüynite, is named after Rene Just Haüy (1743–1822), a French pioneer in crystallography. It was first discovered in 1807 among Vesuvian lavas on Mount Somma in Italy. This rare gem is best known for its astonishing blue color, although microscopic crystals can be found in many other colors, such as green, gray, red, and yellow. Haüyne is related to sodalite and lazurite (lapis lazuli).

Properties and characteristics: Haüyne is a feldspathoid and a member of the sodalite group of minerals. Haüyne crystallizes in the isometric system, and forms translucent, vitreous, and usually twinned crystals that vary enormously in their coloration, ranging from blue, white, and gray, through pink, yellow, and green. Gems are seldom flawless, and usually contain slight to light inclusions. However, even moderately included material is exquisite, due to its electrifying and unusual color.

Cutting, setting, and valuing: Haüyne is a rare gem, although more material has become available in recent decades. Stones are usually very small, although high-quality material of up to about one carat is available and highly prized. Gems greater than this size are rarely available. Small haüyne stones are typically faceted as brilliants to bring out their distinctive fiery colors. Because cutting is difficult and the material is soft, haüyne is normally faceted for collectors only.

Refractive index:	1.494–1.50
Birefringence:	none
Dispersion:	low
Specific gravity:	2.4
Hardness:	5–6
Cleavage:	good in four directions
Fracture:	conchoidal
Luster:	vitreous to greasy
Notable locations:	Germany (Eifel) and Italy
Color:	blue, also white, gray, yellow, green, pink, colorless

Cubic Haüyne

Lazurite
Lapis Lazuli

Class: silicates (framework silicates)

Crystal system: cubic

Composition: complex silicate

Habit: dodecahedral crystals or cubes; massive

Lapis lazuli is named from the Persian *lazhward*, meaning "blue," and the Latin *lapis* meaning "stone." This versatile stone with its uniquely intense color has been popular for more than 6000 years. It mostly consists of the mineral lazurite, but also contains white calcite and brassy yellow metallic pyrite flecks. For many centuries the only known deposits were found at Sar-i-Sang—in a remote mountain valley in Badakhshan, Afghanistan. The Afghanistan mines continue to produce the highest-grade lapis lazuli, although current political conditions make mining difficult. Today lapis lazuli is also mined in Colorado and in Chile, but material from these sources often contains high levels of calcite.

Properties and characteristics: Lapis lazuli is not a mineral, but a rock consisting of as many as 15 different minerals. It is a metamorphic rock, with varying physical properties and composition. It usually forms through the contact metamorphism of limestone. The chief minerals present in lapis are lazurite, diopside, calcite, and pyrite. The dramatic blue of lazurite is caused by the sulfur, which makes up a key part of its chemistry. At Sar-i-Sang the lapis lazuli occurs as a zone of lenses and veins contained by white marble. Shades vary from deep to pale blue—some of which have purple and even green hues.

Cutting, setting, and valuing: Lapis lazuli's value is determined almost entirely by color, with dark, intense blues with violet or rich purple tones being the most expensive. Fine-grained, homogeneous material has a smooth and well-polished finish that is not present in lower-quality stones. Inclusions of calcite almost always lower the value; however, minor inclusions of pyrite make the stone more valuable. Lapis lazuli has always been fashioned as beads and cabochons, carved, or used in inlays, mosaics, and paint (ultramarine blue).

Refractive index:	1.502–1.522
Birefringence:	none
Dispersion:	low
Specific gravity:	2.81–2.84 (as lapis lazuli)
Hardness:	5–5.5
Cleavage:	imperfect
Fracture:	uneven
Luster:	vitreous to greasy
Notable locations: :	Afghanistan, Burma (Myanmar), Chile, Colorado in the USA, Siberia in Russia
Color:	ultramarine blue

Cubic Lazurite

Scheelite

Class: sulfates

Crystal system: tetragonal

Composition: calcium tungstate

Habit: usually short bipyramidal crystals

Scheelite was named after the German-Swedish chemist and apothecary, Karl Wilhelm Scheele (1742–1786), who proved, in 1781, that scheelite contained tungstic oxide. Because of its softness, this mineral is usually only faceted for collectors. Large crystals have been found in Brazil, Korea, and China.

Properties and characteristics: Scheelite is a calcium tunsgate mineral, and a key tungsten ore. It fluoresces bright blue (or green or yellow, when containing trace amounts of molybdenum) under shortwave ultraviolet light. This characteristic allowed prospectors to distinguish scheelite from other minerals. Scheelite occurs in colorless to white, yellow, orange, and dark brown tetragonal crystals; it may be massive and granular. It is found in granite pegmatites, as well as in rocks that have been contact metamorphosed—in particular, limestones with near granite. It can also occur in quartz veins.

Cutting, setting, and valuing: Well-formed crystals are always popular with gem collectors, and rough is often cut as gemstones when it is clear and free of obvious flaw. Gem scheelite is, however, fragile when cut from transparent material. Because of its high luster, refractive index, and dispersion, gems have a fire that is almost as brilliant as that of diamond. Mount Xuebaoding massif in China has, in the last decade, produced some of the best-quality specimens of scheelite; it is found in tin-tungsten veins there. Until recently, gem scheelite was rare enough to appear only in the most extensive collections. This beautiful stone is now gaining appreciation with a much wider market, and the price has declined accordingly. It is still, however, an expensive gemstone. Step, brilliant, and mixed cuts are most popular.

Refractive index:	1.918–1.934
Birefringence:	0.016
Dispersion:	0.026
Specific gravity:	5.9–6.1
Hardness:	4.5–5
Cleavage:	distinct in two directions
Fracture:	subconchoidal
Luster:	vitreous to adamantine
Notable locations:	Brazil, Mexico, Korea, China
Color:	golden yellow, orange, brown, colorless

Tetragonal Scheelite

Class: oxides and hydroxides

Crystal system: tetragonal

Composition: tin oxide

Habit: short to long prisms with pyramidal terminations

Cassiterite is a tin oxide mineral that is usually opaque, although some specimens can be transparent. Because of its luster and numerous crystal faces, specimens are highly sought after and very striking. The name derives from the Greek *kassiteros* for "tin," or from the Phoenician word *cassiterides*, probably a reference to the islands of Ireland and Britain, which were the ancient sources of tin.

Properties and characteristics: Cassiterite is a minor component in many igneous rocks. Most modern-day sources of cassiterite today are found in alluvial or placer deposits, which contain weathered grains. The best sources of cassiterite are the Bolivian tin mines, where it is found in hydrothermal veins. Chinese tungsten-tin mines have also provided some good material. Currently, major tin production comes from alluvial or placer deposits in Russia and the Far East—specifically Thailand, Indonesia, and Malaysia. Pure cassiterite may be colorless or white (particularly specimens from the Malay Peninsula); however, the stone is more often brown or even black, the color being caused by the presence of iron or other trace elements. Occasionally, opaque cassiterite is red.

Cutting, setting, and valuing: Cassiterite is almost as hard as quartz, thereby making it an exceptional cut gemstone. It is, however, very brittle. Brilliant and mixed cuts are most common. The reddish-brown stones are the most rare, and therefore the most valuable. Quality crystals can, however, be hard to find in all of the color variations. Cut stones of good clarity over one carat are rare, but the discovery of Chinese deposits have made them more available.

Refractive index:	2.00–2.10
Birefringence:	0.098
Dispersion:	0.071
Specific gravity:	6.95
Hardness:	6.5
Cleavage:	imperfect in two directions
Fracture:	subconchoidal to uneven
Luster:	adamantine to greasy
Notable locations:	La Paz and Colquiri areas of Bolivia; Cornwall in England, Durango in Mexico, Malaysia, Indonesia, Russia, Thailand, China
Color:	purple, wine, black, reddish brown, or yellow

Tetragonal Cassiterite

Scapolite
Marialite-Meionite Series

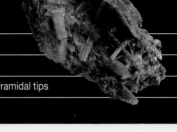

Class: silicates (framework silicates)

Crystal system: tetragonal

Composition: complex silicate

Habit: prismatic crystals with low-angle pyramidal tips

Scapolite comes from the Greek word *scapos*, meaning "rod" or "shaft" and *lithos*, meaning "stone;" this mineral is mainly found in squat or elongated prismatic crystals. Scapolite is also known as wernerite, in honor of the German geologist A. G. Werner (1749–1817). Gem scapolite was originally discovered in 1913 in the Mogok Stone Tract in upper Burma (Myanmar). There, white, pink, yellowish, or violet stones of high quality are found, including cat's eyes.

Properties and characteristics: Scapolite is a silicate of aluminum, and it crystallizes in the tetragonal system. The crystals are frequently found in metamorphic rocks. Yellow, purple, and colorless are the most common gem colors. It can be very difficult to differentiate faceted scapolite from quartz because these two stones share so many gemological properties. However, this mineral is one of the most fluorescent and phosphorescent around. If placed for a few minutes under shortwave ultraviolet, scapolite can remain phosphorescent for more than six hours. Tenebresence is the name given to a color change stimulated by sunlight: some colorless scapolite undergoes a profound change of color under UV light (a component of sunlight), becoming a wonderful saturated, medium blue that is, unfortunately, not permanent. Inclusions of dark minerals are common.

Cutting, setting, and valuing: Less transparent scapolite can be cut as cabochons that will often exhibit a good cat's eye effect. In some cases, when the cat's eye is not distinct, it can exhibit a play of light rather like moonstone (see page 220). Colorless scapolite is less common than other colors. It is most often cut in brilliant or step cuts.

Refractive index:	1.540–1.577
Birefringence:	0.009–0.020
Dispersion:	0.017
Specific gravity:	2.60–2.71
Hardness:	6
Cleavage:	distinct in several directions
Fracture:	subconchoidal to uneven
Luster:	vitreous to resinous
Notable locations:	Afghanistan, Brazil, Madagascar, Tanzania, Burma (Myanmar)
Color:	pink, violet, blue, yellow, gray, colorless; also red-brown cat's eyes

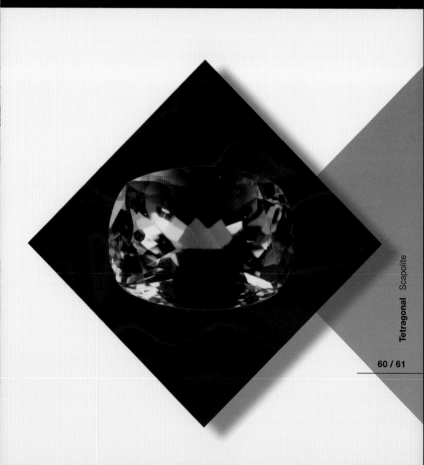

Tetragonal Scapolite

Rutile

Class: oxides and hydroxides

Crystal system: tetragonal

Composition: titanium oxide

Habit: prisms with pyramidal terminations

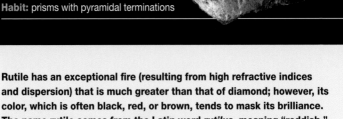

Rutile has an exceptional fire (resulting from high refractive indices and dispersion) that is much greater than that of diamond; however, its color, which is often black, red, or brown, tends to mask its brilliance. The name rutile comes from the Latin word *rutilus*, meaning "reddish," an allusion to its most common color variation. In the past, rutile was polished to parade its dark color, and it was a regular feature of antique mourning jewelry.

Properties and characteristics: Rutile is one of the three forms of titanium dioxide found in nature. It is found as a primary mineral in some late-stage igneous rocks, and it is also a secondary mineral in alluvial deposits and beach sands. This is caused by titanium-bearing minerals—such as titanite and some micas—breaking down. Microscopic inclusions of rutile in quartz, tourmaline, ruby, sapphire, and other gemstones produce magnificent light effects such as chatoyancy (cat's eye effect) and asterism (a star effect that appears as two or more intersecting bands of light across the surface of a gem). Minas Gerais, Brazil, currently produces the highest-grade rutile, but the gemstone is also found in the US, and China.

Cutting, setting, and valuing: A beautiful gemstone comprising clear quartz with large inclusions of golden rutile needles is called rutilated quartz (see also Quartz with Inclusions, page 102). It is sometimes known as Venus's hair or Cupid's darts. Usually cut en cabochon, it is a popular semiprecious gemstone and is also often used in carvings. Cat's eye rutile from Sri Lanka is cut en cabochon. Colorless synthetic rutile is cut as brilliants to simulate diamond.

Refractive index:	2.62–2.90
Birefringence:	0.287
Dispersion:	0.280
Specific gravity:	4.2+
Hardness:	6–6.5
Cleavage:	good in two directions
Fracture:	conchoidal to uneven
Luster:	vitreous to metallic
Notable locations:	Minas Gerais in Brazil, Georgia and California in the USA, Sri Lanka, China
Color:	black or reddish brown in large thick crystals; golden yellow or silvery as inclusions; the synthetic is usually colorless

Tetragonal Rutile

Class: silicates (silicates with isolated silica units)

Crystal system: tetragonal

Composition: zirconium silicate

Habit: doubly terminated prisms with pyramidal tips

Zircon is best known as a colorless diamond imitation, but it appears in many other colors. The name is derived from the Persian *zargun* which means "gold color." Zircon comes in two gemologically distinct varieties: high zircon, with high values of refractive index and birefringence; and low zircon, which is practically isotropic and usually quite radioactive. Zircon is not the artificial gem material cubic zirconia (zirconium oxide).

Properties and characteristics: Zircon is a silicate mineral, zirconium silicate. Its high refractive index and dispersion make it comparable to diamonds in terms of fire and brilliancy. Zircon is a widespread accessory mineral in acid igneous rocks; it also occurs in detrital deposits and metamorphic rocks. Because zircon is a brittle mineral, it tends to chip easily. Prior to cutting, many stones are heat treated to alter the color—usually to yellows, blues, or colorless stones. Color tends to be unevenly distributed, although this can be adjusted to some extent with heat. Some stones that have been heat treated to a deep, sky-blue may fade with prolonged exposure to the sun. Brown and red zircons are usually naturally colored. Low zircons are usually yellowish green, and often show eye-visible growth zoning, giving them a "sleepy" look.

Cutting, setting, and valuing: Zircon is not uncommon, and it is a fairly inexpensive and attractive gemstone. It is usually cut in round brilliants to take advantage of the high dispersion and refractive index. Cushion, zircon, baguette, and mixed cuts are also popular. Bright, sky- or electric-blue stones are the most highly prized, with red, orange, green, and yellow stones being of secondary popularity. Run-of-the-mill blues are considerably less valuable, and stones with a mixed hue or coloration do not fetch the same price as pure stones. It is unusual to find clean stones larger than 10 carats.

Birefringence:	0–0.059
Dispersion:	0.039
Specific gravity:	3.95–4.8
Hardness:	7–7.5
Cleavage:	imperfect in two directions
Fracture:	conchoidal
Luster:	vitreous to adamantine
Notable locations:	Sri Lanka, Burma (Myanmar), Cambodia, Vietnam, Thailand, Norway
Color:	brown, red, yellow, green, blue, black, colorless

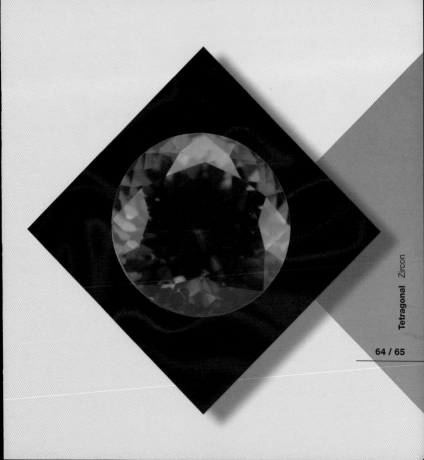

Tetragonal Zircon

Vesuvianite

Class: silicates (silicates with isolated silica units)

Crystal system: tetragonal

Composition: hydrous calcium magnesium aluminum silicate

Habit: short pyramids or long prismatic crystals

Vesuvianite was named in 1795 by the German mineralogist Abraham Gottlob Werner (1749–1817), after Mount Vesuvius, where the mineral was first found. The French mineralogist René Just Haüy (1743–1822) suggested it should be named idocrase (from the Greek word for "mixed form," which alludes to the fact that its crystals show faces resembling a mixture of minerals), and it sometimes goes by this name. Cyprine is a blue variety of vesuvianite (copper impurities giving the blue color, and the name deriving from cyprium, the ancient term for copper). Californite is a compact massive form of vesuvianite, and it resembles jade.

Properties and characteristics: Vesuvianite is a green, brown, yellow, purple, or blue silicate mineral that mainly occurs as tetragonal crystals in skarn deposits and contact metamorphic limestones. Vesuvianite is composed of calcium, magnesium, and aluminum silicate, and it may also contain some beryllium and fluorine. A proportion of its crystal structure resembles that of cubic grossular garnets. "Watermelon" garnet contains both pink hydrogrossular and green vesuvianite (see also Grossular Garnet, page 34).

Cutting, setting, and valuing: Vesuvianite is a fairly common, handsome mineral that is sometimes cut for mineral collectors (it is rarely cut for jewelry). Cabochons and mixed, step, and brilliant cuts are most common, but fine small pinkish purple crystals from Quebec are faceted, as are transparent samples from Pakistan. Transparent or strongly translucent material, in attractive greens or browns, is occasionally used for jewelry, particularly in the south of Italy. Peridot and green garnet are sometimes substituted for vesuvianite. Peridot has a greater specific gravity and is more vibrant in color, while green garnet tends to be heavier and harder than vesuvianite.

Refractive index:	1.700–1.721
Birefringence:	0–0.021
Dispersion:	0.019
Specific gravity:	3.32–3.47
Hardness:	6.5
Cleavage:	poor
Fracture:	subconchoidal to uneven
Luster:	vitreous to resinous
Notable locations:	Asbestos, Quebec in Canada; California and New England in the USA, Mt. Vesuvius in Italy, Ural Mountains in Russia, Switzerland, Pakistan
Color:	usually green, but also brown, yellow, blue, and purple

Tetragonal Vesuvianite

Tugtupite

Class: silicates (framework silicates)

Crystal system: tetragonal

Composition: sodium aluminum beryllium silicate chloride

Habit: usually fine-grained or massive

The unusual and delightfully colored stone tugtupite is found only in the Arctic. Its Inuit name, tuttupit, means "reindeer blood." This "reindeer stone" was first discovered as a gemstone in 1957, at Tugtup Agtakôrfia, Ilimaussaq in Greenland, and it was subsequently named for this location. To date it has only been found in two other locations—Mount St. Hilaire in Quebec, Canada, and the Kola Peninsula in Russia. However, only tugtupite from Greenland has the deep, rich colors that make it so valuable as a gemstone.

Properties and characteristics: Tugtupite is composed of sodium, aluminum, beryllium, silicon, oxygen, and chlorine, and it is extremely fluorescent. Pale reddish colors deepen when the stone is taken into the sunlight, and when placed in the dark, the color then fades to a softer hue again. Tugtupite from the Ilimaussaq massif fluoresces dim red under shortwave ultraviolet radiation and pale salmon orange under longwave. Inclusions are common in most tugtupite. This rare mineral shares a similar crystal structure with sodalite, and the two minerals are occasionally found together in the same sample—producing some uniquely fluorescent material. Tugtupite occurs in high-alkali intrusive igneous rocks.

Cutting, setting, and valuing: Because tugtupite gems occur in massive habit, they are almost always cut en cabochon. They are prized for their very active fluorescence, and brilliant coloration. Finished cabochons are often veined, which gives them a distinctive and interesting appearance. Most faceted transparent gems are less than half of a carat. Specimens from Greenland—both jewelry rough and mineral specimens—are the most highly prized, and coveted by collectors.

Refractive index:	1.492–1.502
Birefringence:	0.006–0.008
Dispersion:	low
Specific gravity:	2.30–2.57
Hardness:	6.5
Cleavage:	distinct
Fracture:	conchoidal
Luster:	vitreous
Notable locations:	Greenland, Russia, Canada
Color:	white, pink to crimson, rarely blue or green

Tetragonal Tugtupite

Emerald
Beryl

Class: silicates (ring silicates)

Crystal system: hexagonal

Composition: beryllium aluminum silicate

Habit: flat-topped prisms, some trapiches

Emerald is the most precious variety of the mineral beryl. The name comes from the Greek word *smaragdos*, by way of the Old French *esmeralde* and means simply "green gemstone." The vibrant green of a good emerald is probably unparalleled in the world of gems.

Properties and characteristics: Emerald's green color is the result of small amounts of chromium and/or vanadium. Unlike other beryl gems, emeralds often contain inclusions, which are considered part of the character of the stone and confirm to the purchaser that the stone is natural. Emerald is mined almost exclusively from hard rocks, where the emerald has grown into small veins or on the walls of cavities. Colombia is the world center of emerald mining. The Muzo mine, north of Bogotá, produces good-quality stones that are a beautiful deep green. In Brazil, various deposits in Bahia, Goias, and Minas Gerais produce noteworthy stones. These are not usually as vivid as those found in Colombia, and the inclusions are usually different. Rare emerald cat's eyes are found in both countries. Brazil is also a source of extremely rare emeralds with six-ray stars. Trapiche emeralds from Colombia look like black-rayed stars, but are crystals intergrown with their host rocks.

Cutting, setting, and valuing: Because of the inclusions, emeralds tend to be more fragile than other beryls and must be handled more carefully. Top-quality, untreated stones (with certification) attract a much higher price than treated stones. The most popular and valuable color is a slightly bluish green in a medium dark tone with strong to vivid saturation. Very large, top-quality stones are rare. The emerald cut is most popular, developed for this unique gem, but other, mainly classical shapes are also used, such as pear-shape, heart-shape, brilliant, and, if there are a lot of inclusions, cabochons or emerald beads.

Refractive index:	1.565–1.602
Birefringence:	0.005–0.010
Dispersion:	0.014
Specific gravity:	2.67–2.78
Hardness:	7.5–8
Cleavage:	one direction, poor
Fracture:	conchoidal
Luster:	vitreous
Notable locations:	Colombia, Brazil, and Zimbabwe; also Australia, Austria, India, Canada, Egypt, USA, Norway, Pakistan, Afghanistan, Russia
Color:	emerald green, green, slightly bluish green

Hexagonal Emerald

Aquamarine
Beryl

Class: silicates (ring silicates)

Crystal system: hexagonal

Composition: beryllium aluminum silicate

Habit: prisms, sometimes with pyramidal faces, sometimes etched all over

Aquamarine is a transparent or translucent variety of beryl, and its subtle blue or turquoise color suggests the tint of seawater. In fact, the name comes directly from the Latin words for "sea water" (*aqua marina*). Stones range from being almost colorless through to sea green or an intermediate, sky blue. Stones from the bluer end of the spectrum tend to be the most popular.

Properties and characteristics: A mining region rich in pegmatite dikes in the state of Minas Gerais in Brazil has been the primary source of gem beryl and several other species of colored gemstones for many years—including large aquamarine crystals. Gem-quality crystals can be up to 3 feet (1 meter) in length, and completely flawless. Their blue color is created by the presence of atoms of ferrous iron in the structure of the crystal. Ferric iron produces yellow tints. The Maxixe mine in the Piaui Valley is home to a dark blue alkali beryl, which is known as Maxixe beryl and was first discovered in 1917. Although some naturally colored Maxixe beryl is believed to be lightfast, most of the Maxixe beryl seen recently in international markets has been artificially colored by exposure to radiation, and it tends to fade to pale yellow or colorless when exposed to light.

Cutting, setting, and valuing: Most of the largest and finest aquamarines are from Brazil, Afghanistan, or Pakistan. The most desirable color is pure blue. In order to attain this hue, many stones are heat treated to remove yellow tinges and make the blue much deeper. Aquamarine is a moderately priced stone—more expensive than blue topaz, for example, but not as costly as emeralds. Step cuts (emerald cuts) are the most popular. Cat's eye or even star-stones can be found, and they are cut as cabochons.

Refractive index:	1.567–1.590
Birefringence:	0.005–0.008
Dispersion:	0.014
Specific gravity:	2.66–2.80
Hardness:	7.5–8
Cleavage:	one direction, poor
Fracture:	conchoidal to uneven
Luster:	vitreous
Notable locations:	Minas Gerais in Brazil, Colorado in the USA, Madagascar, Nigeria, Pakistan, India, Afghanistan, Russia, Zambia
Color:	blue-green, green-blue, blue

Hexagonal Aquamarine

Heliodor
Beryl

Class: silicates (ring silicates)

Crystal system: hexagonal

Composition: beryllium aluminum silicate

Habit: prisms, sometimes with pyramidal
faces, sometimes etched all over

Heliodor is colored by ferric iron. The name heliodor is derived from the Greek *helios* meaning "sun" and *doron* meaning "gift." The name was first used for a beautiful golden beryl that was mined in South West Africa in the early twentieth century. It was announced that heliodor was a different and superior form of yellow beryl, claims that were later proved to be untrue. The name heliodor is now applied to all yellow or golden beryls.

Properties and characteristics: Heliodor appears in a wide range of yellows, from very pale through to orange, or almost green. Its color is the result of trace amounts of iron impurities in the fabric of the beryl, and depending upon the concentrations of iron, and its oxidation state, the color varies. Heliodor crystals form in very distinctive hexagonal prisms, and the crystals are some of the largest found in the gem world. The largest faceted heliodor stone was 2054 carats.

Cutting, setting, and valuing: Heliodor is one of the more commonly found beryl varieties and is priced moderately. Large, flawless stones are fairly rare and therefore naturally command higher prices. Beryl can be cut into a wide spectrum of many-faceted shapes; modern cutters may include concave facets or naturally etched faces in their cut stones. Beryls are particularly well-suited to rectangular or square cuts, as these bring out the stones' transparency and define their color.

Refractive index:	1.567–1.590
Birefringence:	0.005–0.008
Dispersion:	0.014
Specific gravity:	2.66–2.73
Hardness:	7.5–8
Cleavage:	one direction, poor
Fracture:	conchoidal
Luster:	vitreous
Notable locations:	Russia, Brazil, Madagascar, Namibia, USA, Ukraine
Color:	yellow through golden yellow

Hexagonal Heliodor

Goshenite
Beryl

Class: silicates (ring silicates)

Crystal system: hexagonal

Composition: beryllium aluminum silicate

Habit: tabular crystals or prisms

Goshenite is the name for the transparent, colorless beryl that was discovered in Goshen, Hampshire County, Massachusetts; the term has since been applied to all colorless transparent beryl. For centuries, colorless beryl has been used as a substitute for other colorless gemstones, largely because of its excellent qualities. It is sometimes mounted in a "closed" setting, with silver, red, or green foil laid behind it, to produce imitation diamonds, rubies, and emeralds.

Properties and characteristics: The two most prolific sources of goshenite are Russia and North America, but it is found in many other parts of the world. Like most other forms of beryl, goshenite can be quite brittle. Because some trace elements in stones often create their color, one might think that goshenite is pure; this is not, however, the case, since some trace elements do not cause colors. Goshenite may turn yellow-orange (resembling heliodor) or blue (Maxixe-color) if it is exposed to gamma-rays; however, these colors are not stable in daylight.

Cutting, setting, and valuing: Even larger goshenite stones are modestly priced. This is the result of goshenite's lack of color and relative abundance, compared to other beryls. However, high prices are offered for stones that are artistically cut and fashioned, and entirely clear. Goshenite is not used extensively in jewelry, and is normally cut as a brilliant, step, or mixed facet. Goshenite with inclusions or impurities is not usually suitable for gemstones, but may be used in other industries or, if the inclusions are attractive, may appeal to gem collectors.

Refractive index:	1.566–1.600
Birefringence:	0.005–0.009
Dispersion:	0.014
Specific gravity:	2.66–2.90
Hardness:	7.5–8
Cleavage:	one direction, poor
Fracture:	conchoidal
Luster:	vitreous
Notable locations:	Russia, Mexico, Brazil, Canada, USA
Color:	colorless

Hexagonal Goshenite

Morganite
Beryl

Class: silicates (ring silicates)

Crystal system: hexagonal

Composition: beryllium aluminum silicate

Habit: tabular crystals with pyramidal faces

Morganite is a transparent to translucent pink gem variety of beryl. It usually contains cesium and lithium, but the stone's pink color comes from the presence of manganese. Morganite is often heat-treated to create a purer pink color, and to remove any spots or tinges of yellow, which detract from its appearance and value. The mineral was named after J. Pierpoint Morgan (1837–1913), the American industrialist and gem collector who was, by the turn of the century, one of the USA's most important collectors. The chief gemologist for Tiffany & Co., George Kunz, in 1911 named the newly found beryl gem after his most important customer. Some deep orangy pink morganite from Madagascar is now considered to be the new mineral pezzotaite.

Properties and characteristics: Morganite is also known as pink beryl and rose beryl. Color banding is common in morganite, as are inclusions, including "veils" and long hollow tubes containing liquid. Morganite tends to be found in short tabular prisms, and is dichroic (Greek for "two colored" morganite is pale pink and darker purplish pink when seen in two different directions of polarized light). Today this gemstone is mainly mined in Brazil, Madagascar, Afghanistan, Pakistan, and California, USA.

Cutting, setting, and valuing: Morganite is one of the more expensive beryls and like virtually all good pink stones, it commands a high price. In the past, attempts were made to corner the market in morganite beryl, marketing it as "pink emerald." Today, although it is not as expensive as emerald, collectors can expect to pay as much for morganite as they would for fine-quality aquamarine. Common cuts include brilliant and step cuts. When determining the quality of a morganite, the color and clarity are the most important criteria.

Refractive index:	1.572–1.600
Birefringence:	0.008–0.009
Dispersion:	0.014
Specific gravity:	2.71–2.90
Hardness:	7.5–8
Cleavage:	one direction, poor
Fracture:	conchoidal
Luster:	vitreous
Notable locations:	Brazil, Madagascar, Pakistan, Mozambique, Namibia, USA, Afghanistan
Color:	pink, rose, peach

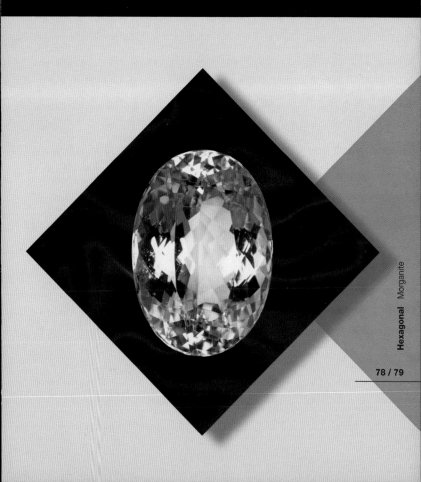

Red Beryl

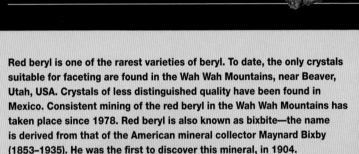

Class: silicates (ring silicates)

Crystal system: hexagonal

Composition: beryllium aluminum silicate

Habit: flat-topped prisms

Red beryl is one of the rarest varieties of beryl. To date, the only crystals suitable for faceting are found in the Wah Wah Mountains, near Beaver, Utah, USA. Crystals of less distinguished quality have been found in Mexico. Consistent mining of the red beryl in the Wah Wah Mountains has taken place since 1978. Red beryl is also known as bixbite—the name is derived from that of the American mineral collector Maynard Bixby (1853–1935). He was the first to discover this mineral, in 1904.

Properties and characteristics: It is thought that red beryl forms along fractures, in cavities, or within the host (white, silica-rich volcanic rhyolite), from high-temperature gas or vapor released when the rhyolite magma cooled and crystallized. Red beryl crystals range in color from orange-red to purplish red, and their color is the result of manganese in the stone. To date, the largest crystal ever found was approximately 54 carats, and the largest cut stone is about eight carats. Red beryl's color is permanent and does not change in the presence of either heat or light.

Cutting, setting, and valuing: Red beryl is among the world's rarest and most desired gemstones. Like emerald, another member of the beryl family, it is usually included. Because red beryl is so rare and popular, stones of almost any size, color, or clarity will find a ready market. The highest-quality stones are normally raspberry pink ranging to a slightly purplish red, with minimum inclusions.

Refractive index:	1.564–1.574
Birefringence:	0.004–0.008
Dispersion:	0.014
Specific gravity:	2.66–2.70
Hardness:	7.5–8
Cleavage:	indistinct
Fracture:	conchoidal to uneven
Luster:	vitreous
Notable locations:	Wah Wah mountains in Utah, USA
Color:	orangy to purplish red

Hexagonal Red Beryl

Apatite

Class: phosphates

Crystal system: hexagonal

Composition: calcium phosphate fluoride

Habit: barrel-shaped hexagonal prisms

The apatite group contains several different minerals, depending on the levels of fluorine, chlorine, or hydroxyl; or on strontium replacing calcium. Most gem apatites are calcium fluorapatite, which is now called apatite-(CaF) by mineralogists. The name comes from the Greek word *apatao* meaning "to deceive," mainly because apatite is so similar to other valuable green minerals such as olivine, peridot, and beryl. Important deposits have been found in Mexico (yellow-green gem material) and the Kola Peninsula in Russia.

Properties and characteristics: Apatite is found in a wide range of colors, which is partly why it is so often confused with other minerals. These include white, yellow, green, violet, blue, brown, and gray. Bright, slightly greenish blue apatite (usually from Brazil) is also known as neon apatite. The yellowish green variety is called "asparagus stone" because of its characteristic color. Large crystals occur in pegmatites and some high-temperature hydrothermal veins. Apatite also occurs as larger crystals in metamorphic rocks, especially limestones and skarns that have been metamorphosed. The crystals are transparent to translucent.

Cutting, setting, and valuing: Apatite is often cut as colorful gemstones; however, its softness means that it is not a widely used or expensive gemstone. It is rarely used in ring settings, because it easily scratches. The most valuable are the purple gems. Apatite is not costly, except for stones above four carats, which tend to be very rare. Fibrous blue apatite may be cut en cabochon; other common cuts are baguette, step, or mixed cuts.

Refractive index:	1.63–1.655
Birefringence:	0.002–0.006
Dispersion:	0.013
Specific gravity:	3.16–3.23
Hardness:	5
Cleavage:	indistinct in two directions
Fracture:	conchoidal
Luster:	vitreous
Notable locations:	Durango in Mexico, Namibia, Madagascar, Ontario and Quebec in Canada, California and Maine in the USA, Germany, Russia, Brazil
Color:	usually yellow-green to green, also yellow, neon blue, purple

Hexagonal Apatite

Taaffeite

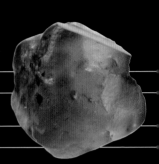

Class: oxides and hydroxides

Crystal system: hexagonal

Composition: beryllium magnesium aluminum oxide

Habit: flattened pyramidal crystals

This rare, exquisite gem is named after Count Edward Charles Richard Taaffe (1898–1967), who discovered the stone by chance from some gems bought in Dublin in 1945. At first it was believed to be spinel, with which it is still often confused, but its birefringence showed it to be a new gem. It was not until 1949 that another stone was found—this time in a parcel of other gems from Sri Lanka. Since 2002, this gem has been known to mineralogists as magnesiotaaffeite-*2N'2S*. Taaffeite is the only mineral to be first discovered as a faceted gemstone instead of a rough crystal.

Properties and characteristics: Taaffeite can easily be mistaken for spinel, and these two gems share very similar gemological properties. The fundamental difference is that taaffeite is doubly refractive (birefringent) while spinel is singly refractive. Taaffeite is also often confused with the rare mineral musgravite. Most faceted and rough taaffeite comes from Sri Lanka, although a few samples have been reported in Tanzania and Burma (Myanmar). Sri Lankan taaffeite is usually found in alluvial deposits (as pebbles), which makes its exact provenance unclear. In other areas, taaffeite crystals are found in granite, amphibolite, and metamorphic limestone. In China, for example, microscopic taaffeite crystals occur in limestone dolomite with granite. The colors vary, depending upon the presence of other minerals. For example, mauve stones (pale mauve is the most common color) are produced by the presence of iron, while purple and red stones derive their color from chromium—with or without iron.

Cutting, setting, and valuing: These gems are currently uncommon, and red and blue stones are very rare. Taaffeite is normally faceted in brilliant and cushion styles, but many are cut "native style" to maximize weight.

Refractive index:	1.716–1.728
Birefringence:	0.004–0.006
Dispersion:	0.019
Specific gravity:	3.61–3.67
Hardness:	8
Cleavage:	absent
Fracture:	conchoidal
Luster:	vitreous
Notable locations:	Sri Lanka, Burma (Myanmar), Tanzania
Color:	mauve, reddish purple, brownish-purple, pink, red, blue, colorless

Hexagonal Taaffeite

Benitoite

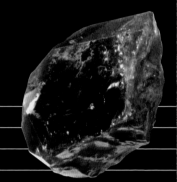

Class: silicates (ring silicates)

Crystal system: hexagonal

Composition: barium titanium silicate

Habit: flat pyramidal triangles or hexagons

Benitoite is a rare, usually blue, silicate mineral, found in serpentine that has been altered hydrothermally. It was first discovered by a prospector in the Diablo Mountain range of San Benito County in California, in 1906. A year later, mineralogist Dr. G. D. Louderback, from the University of California in Berkeley, identified the stone as a new mineral. He named it benitoite "as it occurs near the head waters of the San Benito River in San Benito County." The deep blue of benitoite is comparable to the very best-quality sapphires. It is, however, easily distinguished by its incredibly high birefringence (some five times higher than quartz), and a well-defined dichroism, which makes it appear either blue or colorless when seen in two different directions of polarized light.

Properties and characteristics: Benitoite's birefringence is even higher than that of diamond. Therefore, stones that are well cut show astonishing sparkle. The blue color of benitoite is due to treatments such as heat or irradiation; however, the colorless sections of benitoite crystals have been changed to orange when heated. Benitoite is also very strongly fluorescent under a shortwave ultraviolet light source, turning a very bright, chalky, sky-blue color.

Cutting, setting, and valuing: Benitoite is a prized gemstone and it is extremely rare. There is very high demand for gemstones and rough specimens, and its popularity is continuing to grow. Half-carat stones are not uncommon, but those over one carat are scarce. Despite its attractiveness, benitoite is not often seen in jewelry. Due to scant supply, poor hardness, and fair to poor toughness, its uses are limited. When fashioned for jewelry, brilliant and cushion facets are commonly used. In most cases, the table facet is cut parallel to the main crystal axis to ensure the deepest color.

Refractive index:	1.757–1.804
Birefringence:	0.047
Dispersion:	0.039–0.046
Specific gravity:	3.65–3.68
Hardness:	6-6.5
Cleavage:	poor, indistinct
Fracture:	conchoidal
Luster:	vitreous
Notable locations:	San Benito County, California in the USA
Color:	blue, violet blue, colorless

Hexagonal Benitoite

Rose Quartz and Smoky Quartz

Class: silicates (framework silicates)

Crystal system: trigonal

Composition: silicon dioxide

Habit: commonly massive, sometimes small crystals (rose quartz); striated hexagonal prisms with sets of positive and negative pyramidal terminations (smoky quartz)

Found in nearly every physical environment and as an important constituent of almost every type of rock, quartz is the most common mineral on earth. Rose quartz is one of the more attractive varieties of quartz, and often in demand. The color of massive pink quartz is the result of mineral inclusions that are somewhat like dumortierite; the color of the tiny rose quartz crystals is caused by aluminum, phosphorus, and radiation. Rose quartz is found in Madagascar, India, Brazil, Germany, and the USA. The related smoky quartz is also popular, varying from brown to black, and found, for example, in Brazil, Switzerland, and Colorado, USA.

Properties and characteristics: Some macrocrystalline (large crystal) varieties of quartz are well known and popular as ornamental stones and as gemstones. These include amethyst, citrine, milky quartz, prasiolite (which is leek-green in color), rock crystal, rose quartz, and smoky quartz. Cryptocrystalline (crystals too small to be seen even by a microscope) varieties are also used as gemstones and for ornamental purposes, and are known as chalcedony. If rutile needles are present in the rose quartz then a star effect or asterism is sometimes apparent, and creates a stunning gemstone.

Cutting, setting, and valuing: Although rose quartz is usually too cloudy to be used as a cut gemstone, some outstanding pieces are clear and colorful enough to produce good-quality gems. Most rose quartz is used as cabochons, in which case the clarity is not as important as its color. Smoky quartz is occasionally used for atypical faceted cuts. The commercial market is limited, because there is not huge demand for brown gemstones. Smoky quartz is popular as an ornamental stone and is commonly carved into spheres, pyramids, obelisks, eggs, figurines, and ornate statues. The smoky color can be induced by irradiation.

Refractive index:	1.544–1.553
Birefringence:	0.009
Dispersion:	0.013
Specific gravity	2.65
Hardness:	7
Cleavage:	none
Fracture:	conchoidal to uneven
Luster:	vitreous
Notable locations:	Brazil, Madagascar, Sri Lanka, Maine in the USA
Color:	orangy pink to violet pink (rose quartz); yellow-brown to grayish or dark brown (smoky quartz)

Trigonal Rose Quartz and Smoky Quartz

Rock Crystal
Quartz

Class: silicates (framework silicates)

Crystal system: trigonal

Composition: silicon dioxide

Habit: striated hexagonal prisms with sets of positive and negative pyramidal terminations

Rock crystal is transparent, colorless quartz. Its name derives from the Greek word *krystallos*, meaning "ice." For millennia rock crystal has been used as a gemstone, and carved and polished for ornaments and religious artefacts. Polished rock crystal globes or "crystal balls" were used in medieval times for divination.

Properties and characteristics: Rock crystal is most often found in quartz veins, where it crystallizes inside rock cavities known as vugs (pockets). It is also common in pegmatite dikes. Rock crystal often has inclusions of other minerals; these inclusions combine to create other ornamental stones, which are admired in their own right (see Quartz with Inclusions, page 102). The largest single crystals hail from Brazil, with the largest weighing 100 tons.

Cutting, setting, and valuing: Because such huge crystals are available, the value of rock crystal gems or carvings is dependent upon how well they are cut or fashioned. Rock crystal is a modest gem, and not overly expensive. Large pieces that are free of inclusions are popular with carvers, and it is often used as a "practice stone" for new carvers. Rock crystal does not have sufficient fire or color to be considered a precious stone, but that does not detract from its natural beauty. It is easy to cut, and affordable, making it a standard and admired part of most good collections. Beads and brilliant and step cuts are most common; carved objets d'art are also widely available.

Refractive index:	1.544–1.553
Birefringence:	0.009
Dispersion:	0.013
Specific gravity:	2.65
Hardness:	7
Cleavage:	rhombohedral, rarely seen
Fracture:	conchoidal
Luster:	vitreous
Notable locations:	Arkansas in the USA, St. Gotthard, Switzerland, Brazil, Madagascar, Burma (Myanmar), many others
Color:	colorless

Trigonal Rock Crystal

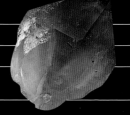

Class: silicates (framework silicates)

Crystal system: trigonal

Composition: silicon dioxide

Habit: striated hexagonal prisms with sets of positive and negative pyramidal terminations

Amethyst is a variety of quartz, and it occurs in a number of different shades of purple, from light pinkish mauve, through violets and deep, almost black or red purples. It is common for amethyst to exhibit one or two secondary hues, in red and/or blue. The name comes from the Hellenic *a-*, meaning "not," and *methustos*, meaning "to intoxicate," an allusion to the belief that you could not get drunk if imbibing wine from an amethyst goblet.

Properties and characteristics: Amethyst's color was originally believed to be due to the presence of manganese; however, it is now known to be caused by trace amounts of ferric iron with radiation damage. When amethyst is heat treated, it becomes yellow like its cousin citrine. Naturally colored crystals that are part-citrine and part-amethyst are known as ametrine. Amethyst is abundantly produced in the state of Rio Grande do Sul in Brazil and in neighboring Uruguay, where it occurs in large geodes (hollow crystal-lined spheres that occur in sedimentary and certain volcanic rocks). Zambia is another important amethyst producer. Different localities can produce amethysts that are unique to that particular region or even to a particular mine.

Cutting, setting, and valuing: Once considered to be one of the most valuable gemstones, alongside diamonds, rubies, and emeralds, amethyst has, since the 1700s, become much less expensive, as a result of the discovery of noteworthy deposits in Brazil and other places. Because the color is frequently distributed patchily throughout the crystals, amethyst is often cut as brilliant round cuts to make the most of the color. Faceted cuts (baguette, mixed, step, and brilliant, when the color is evenly distributed), cabochon, carvings, and beads are common.

Refractive index:	1.544–1.553
Birefringence:	0.009
Dispersion:	0.013
Specific gravity:	2.65
Hardness:	7
Cleavage:	rhombohedral, rarely seen
Fracture:	conchoidal
Luster:	vitreous
Notable locations:	Brazil, Uruguay, India, South Africa, Namibia, Madagascar, Zambia, Mexico, Canada, Russia, Bolivia
Color:	violet to purple

Trigonal Amethyst

Citrine
Quartz

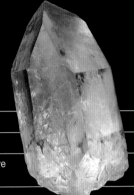

Class: silicates (framework silicates)

Crystal system: trigonal

Composition: silicon dioxide

Habit: striated hexagonal prisms with sets of positive and negative pyramidal terminations

Citrine is a transparent variety of quartz, a member of the silicates family. Its resemblance to topaz makes it a popular stone, and its beautiful yellowish brown color is highly valued. It is a rare gem, and other, more common stones, such as amethyst or smoky quartz, are often treated to create a more citrinelike yellow color. The name citrine is derived from the French word *citron*, meaning "lemon."

Properties and characteristics: Citrine has trace quantities of ferric iron (causing the yellow color), and is rarely found naturally. Brazil is the leading producer of naturally mined citrine, with most of its production coming from the state of Rio Grande do Sul. Citrines whose colors have been produced by heating are often more deeply colored—with hues of orange and red—than the pale yellow of the natural stone.

Cutting, setting, and valuing: The most sought-after heat-treated stones have a clear, radiant yellowish to brownish red hue, and the best-quality stones come from Brazil and Madagascar. Gems in large sizes are available for reasonable prices. Common cuts include brilliants, step cuts, and cabochons. Facets cut in a checkerboard pattern are often used to improve the reflective qualities of the stone. Ametrine, which comprises both amethyst and citrine, is usually cut in a rectangular facet. It can also be cut to blend the two colors, creating movement and patterns throughout. This is one reason why this stone is popular with carvers and imaginative cutters, who can create something approaching a landscape in the finished product.

Refractive index:	1.544–1.553
Birefringence:	0.009
Dispersion:	0.013
Specific gravity:	2.65
Hardness:	7
Cleavage:	rhombohedral, rarely seen
Fracture:	conchoidal
Luster:	vitreous
Notable locations:	Brazil, Madagascar, Congo
Color:	yellow, golden

Trigonal Citrine

Aventurine
Quartz

Class: silicates (framework silicates)

Crystal system: trigonal

Composition: silicon dioxide

Habit: typically massive

Aventurine is characterized by its translucency and the inclusions of platy minerals, which give a shimmering effect known as aventurescence. It is a form of quartz. Deposits are found in Brazil, India, Austria, Russia, and Tanzania; India produces the majority of the world's aventurine. Its name derives from the Italian phrase *per aventura* meaning "by chance," and it is said to have been the only gem that was simulated by man before its natural equivalent was discovered. This idea comes from the tale of an accidental discovery by a seventeenth-century Italian glassmaker who unwittingly dropped copper filings into molten glass. The result was later dubbed aventurine glass or "goldstone;" it looks similar to natural aventurine, but is completely different in character.

Properties and characteristics: Aventurine quartz is actually a rock known as quartzite, which is not a mineral. It is mainly composed of large grains of crystalline quartz, with grains of other minerals giving the stone its color. Aventurine is most often green; however, it may also be orange, brown, yellow, gray, or blue. Fuchsite (a dark green variety of muscovite) is aventurine's most common inclusion, and provides the stone with a sheen of metallic green or blue. Oranges and browns are normally due to the presence of hematite, goethite, or pyrite. When there are high levels of fuchsite present, aventurine can become opaque. It is also often banded.

Cutting, setting, and valuing: Very fine grades of green aventurine that show few or no sparkling impurities are the most valuable. Most material is carved into beads and figurines, and only the best examples are fashioned into cabochons and set into jewelry. Aventurine quartz is a porous material that takes dye easily, so it is often available in affected, unnatural-looking shades.

Refractive index:	1.55 (spot)
Birefringence:	0.009
Dispersion:	0.013
Specific gravity:	2.64–2.69
Hardness:	7
Cleavage:	none
Fracture:	conchoidal
Luster:	vitreous
Notable locations:	Brazil, India, Austria, Russia, Tanzania
Color:	green, blue-green, greenish brown, peach, yellow, gray

Trigonal Aventurine

Class: silicates (framework silicates)

Crystal system: trigonal

Composition: silicon dioxide

Habit: typically massive

Any quartz crystal or cluster that is white in color, and translucent to opaque, is known as milky quartz. It is the cloudy white character of the crystals that originally led the stone to be dubbed milky. Cloudy patches that appear inside otherwise clear rock quartz, amethyst, citrine, or smoky quartz are often caused by milky quartz. The milky quartz may have formed at an early stage of the crystal's growth and then been covered by a clear quartz material later. The result appears almost like a crystal within a crystal; the inside crystal may have a ghostly appearance, giving this gemstone the alternative name "phantom quartz."

Properties and characteristics: Milky quartz occurs in metamorphic and igneous rocks and is a very common vein-filling mineral. The white color comes from fine-scale gas, liquid, or solid inclusions trapped within the growing quartz. Milky quartz is usually massive, but well-formed crystals (hexagonal prisms with pyramidal ends) are also common. Since quartz can be found in gold veins, massive quartz containing small particles or crystals of gold is known as "gold quartz" and used in jewelry. Milky quartz can also contain, or be colored by, other metals or their ores. Very large crystals are commonly found in Siberia.

Cutting, setting, and valuing: Milky quartz can be faceted as a gem (usually brilliant cut), but is more often sold as raw or tumbled stones, or cut as beads or en cabochon, or used in cameos. Because it is widely available, milky quartz is not expensive, and large examples are common.

Refractive index:	1.544–1.553
Birefringence:	0.009
Dispersion:	0.013
Specific gravity:	2.65
Hardness:	7
Cleavage:	none
Fracture:	conchoidal to uneven
Luster:	vitreous
Notable locations:	Brazil, Madagascar, Russia, Namibia, Germany, Greece, England; New York, New Hampshire, Rhode Island, Alaska, and California in the USA
Color:	various shades of white, usually milky

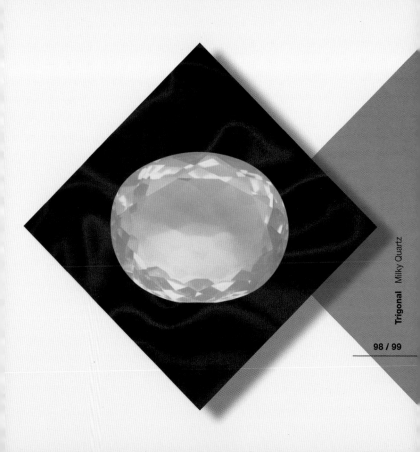

Trigonal Milky Quartz

Chatoyant Quartz

Class: silicates (framework silicates)

Crystal system: trigonal

Composition: silicon dioxide

Habit: typically massive

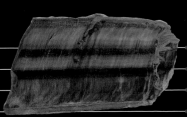

Chatoyant quartz is a compact quartz with fine parallel cavities, or parallel needles of any fibrous mineral. When polished, this type of quartz exhibits a cat's eye (which looks like a narrow light streak that runs from one end of the mineral to the other). The word chatoyant is, in fact, coined from the French *oeil de chat*, meaning "cat's eye." Tiger's eye, also known as crocidolite cat's eye, is the best-known variety of chatoyant quartz. It has rich yellow and golden brown stripes, with a fine golden luster when polished. Hawk's eye (also called falcon's eye) is blue-gray or blue-green, and rarer than tiger's eye. There is also a reddish-brown variety (sometimes called cherry tiger's eye) created by heat-treatment of tiger's eye. Australian tiger's eye with hematitic jasper bands is sometimes called "tiger iron" instead.

Properties and characteristics: Quartz cat's eyes come from Sri Lanka and India, and are honey-yellow or gray and white; they are translucent, not opaque. Tiger's eye is golden brown, with iron-oxide staining giving the stripes. It is a quartz with altered inclusions of crocidolite (blue asbestos) creating the effect. Hawk's eye is a blue variant. Pietersite is a breccia composed usually of tiger's eye and sometimes hawk's eye. Discovered in the 1960s in Namibia, pietersite has gained a devoted following among collectors who cherish its dramatic patterns in red, gold, blue, and black. It is also found in China.

Cutting, setting, and valuing: Cutting is important with cat's eye because the rough material reveals little of the chatoyancy of the finished gem. The cat's eye effect is best shown when the stone is cut en cabochon, with the fibers or fibrous structures parallel to the base. Larger stones are more expensive. For the less expensive tiger's eye, beads and polished stones are also popular.

Refractive index:	1.544–1.553
Birefringence:	0.009
Dispersion:	0.013
Specific gravity:	2.65
Hardness:	7
Cleavage:	none
Fracture:	conchoidal to uneven
Luster:	vitreous
Notable locations:	Sri Lanka, South Africa, Burma (Myanmar), India, Australia, China
Color:	blue-green, golden brown, green-gray, and reddish brown

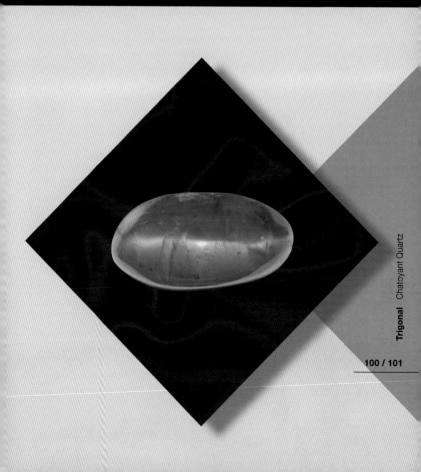

Trigonal Chatoyant Quartz

Quartz with Inclusions

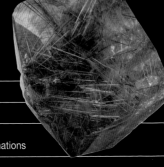

Class: silicates (framework silicates)

Crystal system: trigonal

Composition: silicon dioxide

Habit: striated hexagonal prisms with sets of positive and negative pyramidal terminations

Many minerals may be found as inclusions in quartz. Technically, an inclusion is material that is different from the chief elements of the host, found within the body of a crystal. Tourmaline, chlorite, ajoite, papagoite, hematite, limonite, kaolinite, hydrocarbons, and rutile are just some of the materials that occur as inclusions in quartz, and each produces a different effect. Clear prisms of quartz that reveal attractive displays of the inclusions they host are known as "scenic" or "garden" quartz.

Properties and characteristics: The most popular quartz with inclusions is rutilated quartz (or sagenite). It is transparent rock crystal with golden, silvery, or red needles of rutile displayed in patterns within it. Each pattern is different and some are extraordinarily beautiful. The inclusions are sometimes called Venus hair or Cupid's darts. Less well known is a variety called tourmalinated quartz which, instead of rutile, has black or dark green tourmaline crystals contained within it. Opaque, metallic inclusions of gold and silver are also possible, as well as branchlike, silvery, gray, or black dendrites of manganese and iron oxides. Even gas bubbles can make impressive quartz inclusions.

Cutting, setting, and valuing: When cut en cabochon, quartz containing inclusions may show a chatoyant (cat's eye) effect; this cutting style can also magnify the inclusions. Brilliant and step cuts, and beads are also used. A rutile/hematite starburst is probably the most sought-after type of quartz with inclusions. Phantoms, "starbursts," "flowers," "snowflakes," and dendrites are valuable and in great demand with collectors. The value is related to the rarity, distinctiveness, and beauty of the inclusions; the more centrally placed and less obscured it is, the higher the value.

Refractive index:	1.544–1.553
Birefringence:	0.009
Dispersion:	0.013
Specific gravity:	2.65
Hardness:	7
Cleavage:	rhombohedral, rarely seen
Fracture:	conchoidal to uneven
Luster:	vitreous
Notable locations:	Madagascar, Brazil, South Africa, India, Sri Lanka, Germany, Switzerland, USA
Color:	colorless with inclusions of red, black, yellow, gold, green, blue, gray

Agate
Chalcedony

Class: silicates (framework silicates)

Crystal system: trigonal

Composition: silicon dioxide

Habit: massive or concentrically zoned, banded; may be fibrous

Agate is the commonest ornamental fibrous chalcedony (a form of quartz). Agate is similar to crystalline quartz in composition and physical properties, although it is a little softer and lighter in weight. Colors vary greatly, depending upon the impurities contained in the stone. Agate is named after the river Achates in Sicily, where it was found in around 300 BCE. There are many different types of agate. Each agate forms by filling a cavity in a host rock. It is often found in round protuberances, with evenly spaced bands like the rings in the trunk of a tree. The bands can have a lacy shape, or have the appearance of eyes or landscapes.

Properties and characteristics: Agate occurs in knobby masses in rocks such as volcanic lavas. Agates show a wide variety of colors and patterns, and a distinct banding. In ribbon agate, the bands appear as straight lines when viewed in cross section. When white bands alternate with bands of black, red or brown, the stone is known as onyx or sardonyx (see page 108). Ring or eye agates have circular, concentric bands in a variety of colors. Moss agate has inclusions of green-colored matter, which forms unusual patterns that resemble vegetable growth. Agates are often opaque, but they can be translucent, and occasionally almost transparent.

Cutting, setting, and valuing: Because it is porous, agate is often dyed or stained to enhance its natural colors. Agate's value varies depending on its colors and patterns; distinctive patterns, such as landscapes, are the most valuable. Large stones are also sold at a premium. Banded agates are some of the most popular stones, and delicately designed lace agate, often from Mexico, is also highly regarded. Cabochons, cameos, and polished stones are the most common jewelry cuts, and agate is popular for carving.

Refractive index:	1.53–1.54
Birefringence:	0–0.004
Dispersion:	0.013
Specific gravity:	2.57–2.64
Hardness:	6.5
Cleavage:	none
Fracture:	conchoidal, may look splintery because of parallel fibers
Luster:	vitreous to waxy
Notable locations:	Idar-Oberstein in Germany, Mexico, Uruguay, Brazil, USA, China, India, Madagascar, Scotland, Namibia, Russia, Botswana
Color:	banded in shades of gray, red-brown, blue, purple; may be dyed almost any color

Trigonal Agate

Fire Agate
Chalcedony

Class: silicates (framework silicates)

Crystal system: trigonal

Composition: silicon dioxide

Habit: curved masses with iridescent surfaces

Like most agates, fire agate is a layered stone, but with microscopically thin layers of silica and iron oxides that allow the light rays entering them to interfere with each other, making colors known as fire. This rainbow effect, called iridescence, is most familiar in mother of pearl, but it can also be particularly spectacular in fire agate. This agate was discovered in the early 1940s.

Properties and characteristics: Fire agate, like all chalcedonies, is believed to be formed when hot water saturated with colloidal silica (a suspension of silica gel) and iron oxide enters cavities in another rock and begins to cool. This produces alternating layers of silica and iron oxide (known as schiller layers), and creates the brilliant and unique fire of this gem. In high-quality pieces, this iridescent layering is continuous throughout the stone. More commonly, however, the layering is patchy at best, or, when sustained, weak.

Cutting, setting, and valuing: Because of the limited number of gem-quality localities, fire agate is still very rare. Not surprisingly, good specimens command a high price amongst collectors. Because of the layering, which can be uneven, most stones are almost carved rather than cut. En cabochon is the most common cut, used to bring out the iridescence. Mixed facet cuts have been successful to some extent, and beads and cameos are used; however, the abundance of curvy, asymmetrical shapes make fire agate more suitable for custom crafting.

Refractive index:	1.530–1.539
Birefringence:	0.004
Dispersion:	0.013
Specific gravity:	2.57–2.64
Hardness:	6.5
Cleavage:	none
Fracture:	conchoidal
Luster:	vitreous to waxy
Notable locations:	Arizona, Colorado, California in the USA, Mexico
Color:	brown, red, orange

Onyx, Sard, and Sardonyx

Chalcedony

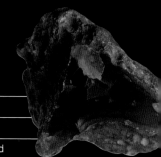

Class: silicates (framework silicates)

Crystal system: trigonal

Composition: silicon dioxide

Habit: massive or concentrically zoned, banded

Onyx is an agate composed of regular bands, each layer showing very different colors. True onyx is black and white. Sardonyx is similar in structure, but red-brown and white in color, and is always banded. The name onyx is derived from the Greek word for fingernail. Legend has it that Cupid cut Venus's fingernails and scattered them on earth where they were turned to stone by the Fates. The name sardonyx is derived from the Greek word *sard* (from Sardis in Turkey), and applies to the brown and white banded variety.

Properties and characteristics: In recent times the name onyx has become confused with other banded materials, in particular calcite formed in cave systems in Mexico and Pakistan and often carved. The name is also used for "black onyx," which is usually chalcedony that has been heat- or acid-treated to turn it black. The bands in onyx are usually straight, which separates it from banded agate, whose lines are generally curved and rounded. Sardonyx is an onyx with bands of red-brown sard alternating with the white or black. Sard is a less saturated, browner color than carnelian, and less vibrant. Sard is sometimes considered to be a synonym for carnelian.

Cutting, setting, and valuing: Black onyx shines particularly well when it is used as a backdrop for other stones. Its fine texture also makes it perfect for carving. Banded onyx and sardonyx are relatively inexpensive and can be found in large sizes. Stones that contain bright orange-red, reddish brown and white bands are particularly popular. Natural sardonyx is rarely found. Onyx is opaque, and most commonly cut en cabochon or as beads. It is also used for cameos and intaglios.

Refractive index:	1.53–1.54
Birefringence:	0–0.004
Dispersion:	0.0013
Specific gravity:	2.57–2.64
Hardness:	6.5
Cleavage:	none
Fracture:	conchoidal
Luster:	vitreous
Notable locations:	India, Russia, Pakistan, USA, Germany, Brazil, Mexico
Color:	onyx is usually black and white, in layers (although can be uniform black); sardonyx is onyx with white and red layers; sard is translucent yellowish chestnut to reddish brown

Chrysoprase
Chalcedony

Class: silicates (framework silicates)

Crystal system: trigonal

Composition: silicon dioxide

Habit: massive, or as veins in rock

The name chrysoprase comes from the Greek *chrysos*, meaning "golden," and *prason*, "leek," which describes the color of the stone. Across the years, this name was applied to several yellowish green gemstones, including beryl, but eventually it became limited to the apple-green, microcrystalline variety of chalcedony. The duller, leek-green stones have been called prase instead. Chrysoprase is found mostly in Australia, although it has been found in Brazil and the Ural Mountains.

Properties and characteristics: Chrysoprase is cryptocrystalline, that is, it has a microscopic crystalline structure. Under high magnification, these crystals look like parallel fibers. Unlike most other green stones, which derive their color from chromium or vanadium, chrysoprase's distinctive green color is the result of included oxidized nickel compounds, such as nickel silicate clay minerals. A rare, related chalcedony in darker, more vibrant shades of green is colored by chromium; it occurs in Zimbabwe and is called mtorolite, but is sometimes sold as "chrome chalcedony."

Cutting, setting, and valuing: Chrysoprase is usually translucent, but poorer quality stones may appear opaque. A small number of chrysoprases are semitransparent and even transparent. If the color is good, these stones fetch a high price. Chrysoprase is usually fashioned into cabochons, beads, and bangles, or it is carved to create jewelry and other ornamental objects. It is easily worked and takes a fine polish. The highest-quality material is a rich, evenly colored apple green, and does not contain any flaws, inclusions, or imperfections. Chrysoprase is among the most valuable of the chalcedonies.

Refractive index:	1.530–1.538
Birefringence:	up to 0.004
Dispersion:	0.013
Specific gravity:	2.57–2.64
Hardness:	6.5
Cleavage:	none
Fracture:	conchoidal
Luster:	vitreous to resinous
Notable locations:	Australia, Brazil, Ural Mountains in Russia, Austria
Color:	pale green, yellowish green, apple green, deep green

Jasper
Chalcedony

Class: silicates (framework silicates)

Crystal system: trigonal

Composition: silicon dioxide

Habit: massive

Jasper has been used for gems and ornamental items for thousands of years. Jasper's name is derived from the Greek word *iaspis*, meaning "spotted stone." Jasper was a much-loved gem in the ancient world; its name can be traced back in Hebrew, Assyrian, Persian, Greek, and Latin. It comes in all colors; the red-flecked green variety is known heliotrope or bloodstone. The coloring in most jaspers is due to iron, often with manganese. Jasper is usually found in association with agate and chalcedony. It is generally considered a member of the chalcedony family, but is sometimes grouped as a quartz because of its grainy structure.

Properties and characteristics: Jasper is an ornamental rock composed mostly of chalcedony or fine-grained quartz with included oxide minerals, which give it colorful bands and patterns. Many trade names have been given to the different types of jasper; for example, apple jasper (golden brownish-red), dalmatian jasper (beige with black spots), fancy jasper (all colors), leopard jasper (brownish red with black spots), and many locality names. Red jasper occurs in India and Venezuela, among other places. The USA produces many colors, including orbicular poppy jasper (which is yellow-to-red with white, pink, or red flower-shaped patterns) in California, and Russia is home to the red-and-green ribbon jasper.

Cutting, setting, and valuing: Jasper is used for ornamental items or as a gemstone. It can be highly polished and is used for vases, seals, and, at one time, snuff boxes. It is of little value and used mostly for inexpensive jewelry and small ornamental objects such as carvings and boxes. Cameos, intaglios, beads, and polished stones are the most common gem shapes, and jasper is also often used in mosaics.

Birefringence:	none
Dispersion:	0.013 for quartz, probably not detectable
Specific gravity:	2.58–2.91
Hardness:	6.5–7
Cleavage:	none
Fracture:	conchoidal
Luster:	vitreous to greasy
Notable locations:	India, Egypt, USA, Canada, Russia, Australia, Madagascar, Brazil
Color:	red, pink, yellow, green, brown, and grayish blue

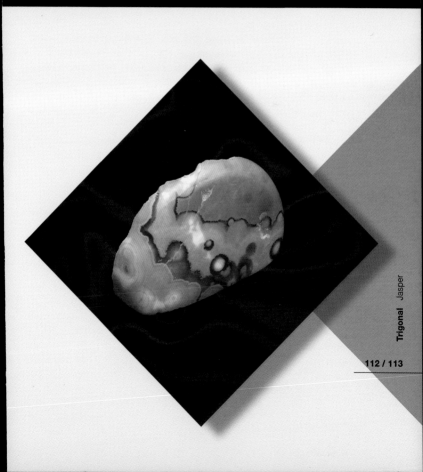

Trigonal Jasper

Carnelian
Chalcedony

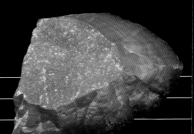

Class: silicates (framework silicates)

Crystal system: trigonal

Composition: silicon dioxide

Habit: massive; may be fibrous

Carnelian is a translucent stone. This quality sets it apart from jasper, which is a similar color, but opaque. Its name derives from *carne*, the Latin for "flesh," probably because of its color. Another name for carnelian was cornelian, perhaps derived from the Latin word *cornus* meaning "dogwood berry." The stone was popular in ancient Greece and Rome, where it was used for cameos, signet rings, and intaglios.

Properties and characteristics: Like other chalcedony varieties, carnelian forms in cavities in rocks from silica-rich solutions. Crystals are too small to be seen, even with a microscope, so it is considered to be a variety of cryptocrystalline quartz. The stone gets its red color from iron oxide (hematite), and the color is intensified when it is heat treated. Rudimentary heat treatment of carnelian has been undertaken for millennia, often in clay pots. The stone can be fairly fibrous looking, and it has a dull, waxy luster. The boundary between orange-red carnelian and reddish brown sard is not strict, and differs from observer to observer.

Cutting, setting, and valuing: Many of the so-called carnelians available are agates that have been dyed and then heat treated. The color distribution of natural carnelian is much cloudier and uneven. The gemstone is normally cut en cabochon, but cameos and beads are also popular. Small stones may be tumbled and polished, and are a feature in many good collections. Carnelian is more valuable than many other chalcedony stones, particularly when it is a pale ruby color (or other pastel shade); however, it is still fairly inexpensive.

Refractive index:	1.53–1.55
Birefringence:	0–0.004
Dispersion:	0.013
Specific gravity:	2.57–2.64
Hardness:	6.5
Cleavage:	none
Fracture:	conchoidal
Luster:	vitreous to waxy
Notable locations:	India, Brazil, Uruguay, Japan
Color:	clear orange red to dark orange brown

Trigonal Carnelian

Bloodstone
Chalcedony

Class: silicates (framework silicates)

Crystal system: trigonal

Composition: silicon dioxide

Habit: massive

Bloodstone is a variety of chalcedony and is green jasper that contains red spots of jasper. The red spots have the appearance of blood, giving the stone its descriptive name. Bloodstone is also known as heliotrope. The name heliotrope is derived from the Greek words *helios*, meaning "sun," and *trepein*, meaning "turning," because of a notion that when the stone was immersed in water it would turn the sun red; polished stones were described as reflecting the sun. Finely ground bloodstone was used as a medicine and aphrodisiac in India.

Properties and characteristics: Bloodstone is dark green jasper, which is a cryptocrystalline variety of quartz, and it contains red to brown inclusions. The red spots are the result of iron oxide, while the green "base" color comes from particles of chlorite or hornblende needles. Bloodstone is sometimes known in the trade as blood jasper. Sometimes yellow and/or other colors of jasper are also present, but these vibrantly colored gemstones are usually known as fancy jasper. Bloodstone is found and mined mainly in India and Australia.

Cutting, setting, and valuing: Bloodstone is cut en cabochon and is popular in signet rings. It is also cut into beads, but is most often used as a sealstone. Polished stones and cameos are also popular. The name *bludstein* (bloodstone) means both hematite and bloodstone in Germany.

Refractive index:	1.54 (spot)
Birefringence:	none
Dispersion:	0.013 for quartz, probably not detectable
Specific gravity:	2.58–2.91
Hardness:	6.5
Cleavage:	none
Fracture:	conchoidal
Luster:	vitreous to waxy
Notable locations:	Australia, Brazil, China, India, Scotland, USA
Color:	green or greenish blue with red spots

Gaspeite

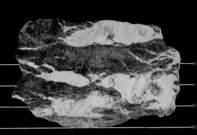

Class: carbonates

Crystal system: trigonal

Composition: nickel carbonate

Habit: usually massive

Gaspeite is named after the locality of its discovery—the Gaspé Peninsula in Quebec, Canada. It was accepted as a separate mineral in 1966. Gaspeite is considered rare, being found in only a few localities, but it is becoming popular in semiprecious stone markets. This pale to apple-green semiprecious stone often contains brown inclusions, derived from its host rock. Far from detracting from gaspeite's beauty, they produce unique designs that can make the stone more valuable.

Properties and characteristics: Gaspeite belongs to the calcite group of minerals, which includes calcite, magnesite, rhodochrosite, siderite, smithsonite, and spherocobaltite. Gaspeite is found as a secondary mineral near nickel sulfide deposits, and is most commonly found in arid or semiarid conditions that encourage the concentration of calcareous or carbonate minerals. It is usually found in massive form; crystals are rare. Gaspeite has a high nickel content, and this gives the stone its distinctive color. Although it was discovered in Canada, the main source is currently a small town in Western Australia, called Widgiemooltha. It has also been found in Japan, South Africa, and Sardinia. Crystals are usually translucent, and the massive material is opaque. Gaspeite looks similar in color to variscite and faustite, green minerals sometimes confused with turquoise.

Cutting, setting, and valuing: This unusual stone has only recently been used in jewelry, and is often set in silver. Gaspeite is used in the jewelry trade for beads, pendants, and carvings, and it is often cut into cabochons. Gaspeite is still relatively inexpensive. It may be polymer-impregnated to harden the surface and intensify the color.

Refractive index:	1.61–1.83
Birefringence:	0.22
Dispersion:	strong
Specific gravity:	3.21
Hardness:	4.5–5.0
Cleavage:	good in three directions
Fracture:	uneven
Luster:	vitreous to dull
Notable locations:	Quebec in Canada, Perth in Australia
Color:	light to bright or olive green

Ruby
Corundum

Class: oxides and hydroxides

Crystal system: trigonal

Composition: aluminum oxide

Habit: steep hexagonal bipyramids or rhombohedra

For millennia, the ruby has been considered one of the most valuable gemstones in the world, and India was widely regarded as the first important source of these gems. The Sanskrit word for ruby is *ratnaraj*, which means "king of the gemstones." The name ruby comes from the Latin word *ruber*, meaning "red." Ruby is a gem-quality variety of the mineral corundum, one of the most durable minerals there is; it is a crystalline form of aluminum oxide. Ruby is the red variety; the non-red varieties are known as sapphires. The best shade of red for ruby is often dubbed pigeon-blood red, but ruby can be any shade of red (including purplish, orangy, or brownish), and star rubies may be almost pink.

Properties and characteristics: Corundum is a common mineral found in metamorphic and igneous rocks. The red color in ruby is caused by trace amounts of the element chromium. Crystal inclusions of rutile or diaspore can cause a six-rayed star effect (known as asterism) to form a "star ruby." Rubies come from all over the world but good gemstones are found in Thailand, India, Madagascar, Zimbabwe, North Carolina in the USA, Afghanistan, Pakistan, Sri Lanka, Kenya, Tanzania, Vietnam, and, most notably, Burma (Myanmar).

Cutting, setting, and valuing: Perfectly transparent rubies are more valuable than those with eye-visible inclusions. The most important factor in the value of a ruby is its color. Larger rubies, because they are much more rare, will cost more per carat than smaller stones of the same quality. In fact, large rubies are more valuable and rarer than even top-quality diamonds. Rubies displaying an asterism are cut into a cabochon. Otherwise, faceted cuts (usually mixed cuts, step, and brilliants) are most commonly used. Inexpensive, low-quality rubies may be filled with lead glass to disguise their color and clarity.

Refractive index:	1.761–1.769
Birefringence:	0.008
Dispersion:	0.018
Specific gravity:	3.99–4.00
Hardness:	9
Cleavage:	weak basal parting
Fracture:	conchoidal
Luster:	adamantine to vitreous
Notable locations:	Burma (Myanmar), Thailand, Sri Lanka, India, Vietnam, Kenya, Tanzania, Madagascar
Color:	red to purplish red (star stones may be reddish pink as well)

Trigonal Ruby

Sapphire
Corundum

Class: oxides and hydroxides

Crystal system: trigonal

Composition: aluminum oxide

Habit: steep hexagonal bipyramids,
or stout columns

When a particular color is not specified, the term sapphire refers to the blue variety of corundum. The finest sapphires are a rich, cornflower blue. In the past, this color was known as Kashmir blue in deference to the traditional source of the finest sapphires. The word sapphire comes from the Latin word for "blue," *sapphirus*, which is also thought to have been used in ancient times to refer to lapis lazuli.

Properties and characteristics: All of the gemstones in the corundum group consist of pure aluminum oxide that crystallized into gemstones as a result of pressure and heat at a great depth. The presence of small amounts of other elements are responsible for the coloring, turning a material that is basically colorless into a blue, red, yellow, pink, or greenish sapphire. For many centuries, there has been considerable debate about which stones fall into the sapphire category. The general consensus was that red stones (colored with chromium) would be known as rubies, while anything that was not "ruby" red would be called a sapphire. Traces of iron and titanium provide sapphires with their blue color. The color of cut stones can vary dramatically.

Cutting, setting, and valuing: Sapphires are faceted in step and brilliant cuts. Stones exhibiting an asterism or other rough inclusion are cut en cabochon. The darker (inky) blue stones that most jewelers carry are not as valuable as bright and lighter-toned blue material. Specialists consider the "Kashmir" color, which is clean and intense, with a very understated hint of violet, to be the best and most valuable of the blues. Some stones of this color were most recently mined in Madagascar in the early 1990s. The "Burmese" color is also highly rated; it ranges from a rich, royal blue to a deep cornflower blue. Top-quality blue sapphires come from metamorphic deposits, and remain rare.

Refractive index:	1.760–1.780
Birefringence:	0.008
Dispersion:	0.018
Specific gravity:	3.98–4.00
Hardness:	9
Cleavage:	weak basal parting
Fracture:	conchoidal
Luster:	adamantine to vitreous
Notable locations:	Sri Lanka, Burma (Myanmar), Thailand, Montana in the USA, Australia, Rwanda, Kenya, Tanzania, Madagascar
Color:	blue; fancy sapphires are any color except red

Trigonal Sapphire

Padparadscha sapphire
Corundum

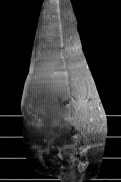

Class: oxides and hydroxides

Crystal system: trigonal

Composition: aluminum oxide

Habit: steep hexagonal bipyramids

Padparadscha (sometimes spelled padparadshah) is an orangy pink sapphire (corundum). This very rare gem is valued for its attractive color. The most important deposits are located in Sri Lanka; some Vietnamese pink sapphires, and African red-orange sapphires come close to being padparadschas. The name derives from the Sinhalese word for lotus blossom. Naturally colored (unheated) padparadscha sapphire is among the rarest and most highly valued corundums in the world.

Properties and characteristics: A large majority of padparadscha sapphires (and most other colors of sapphire) are heated to deepen the color and improve the clarity. The color of the orangy-pink padparadscha sapphire comes from trace quantities of both iron and chromium. The largest gem-quality padparadscha sapphire was a 1126-carat crystal found in Sri Lanka in the mid 1980s. A large faceted example weighs 100.18 carats and can be found in the New York's American Museum of Natural History.

Cutting, setting, and valuing: Padparadscha sapphires are one of the world's most expensive gems, and prices are comparable to those fetched by fine rubies or emeralds, and even diamonds. Padparadscha sapphires must have greater clarity than an equivalent ruby because inclusions seem to be more prominent in a padparadscha sapphire. However, padparadscha sapphires are rarer than rubies, and because they are usually only found in stones of well under two carats, they are highly prized and expensive. The deep, saturated colors are more valuable. Stones are normally faceted as a mixed cut. Beryllium-diffused (treated) orangy-pink sapphires are sometimes incorrectly called padparadschas.

Refractive index:	1.761–1.769
Birefringence:	0.008
Dispersion:	0.018
Specific gravity:	3.98–3.99
Hardness:	9
Cleavage:	weak basal parting
Fracture:	conchoidal
Luster:	adamantine to vitreous
Notable locations:	Sri Lanka
Color:	pinkish orange

Trigonal Padparadscha sapphire

Colorless sapphire
Corundum

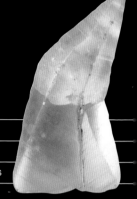

Class: oxides and hydroxides

Crystal system: trigonal

Composition: aluminum oxide

Habit: steep hexagonal bipyramids, or stout columns

Clear colorless corundum is known as white sapphire, colorless sapphire, or leucosapphire. Colorless sapphire is free of the trace elements that impart color. These stones have been occasionally cut as microscope lenses, mainly because they are very hard and highly refractive, and have a weak dispersion. Gem-quality colorless sapphires are not common, and can be quite difficult to obtain. They have, however, been used as a substitute for diamonds for years. Some colorless sapphires have a very light tint of pastel blue, yellow or pink, but they are nevertheless still considered colorless.

Properties and characteristics: Rough colorless sapphires are usually light gray or brown in color when they are mined, and then heated to make them clear. In very rare circumstances, however, they will be found in a clear state. Synthetic corundum was the first gemstone to be reproduced by artificial means using the flame-fusion method, which is also known as the Verneuil process. This method was invented by a French chemist named Auguste Victor Louis Verneuil in 1902. Diamondite, a diamond imitation that was popular in the early 1900s, is, in reality, synthetic colorless sapphire produced by the flame-fusion method.

Cutting, setting, and valuing: White sapphires are most commonly found in round or oval brilliant cut form, surrounding larger colored stones in rings. Synthetic colorless sapphire is many times more common than natural colorless sapphires, and is often used for watch faces.

Refractive index:	1.761–1.769
Birefringence:	0.008
Dispersion:	0.018
Specific gravity:	3.99
Hardness:	9
Cleavage:	weak basal parting
Fracture:	conchoidal
Luster:	adamantine to vitreous
Notable locations:	Sri Lanka
Color:	colorless, sometimes with light tints of pink, blue, or yellow

Trigonal Colorless sapphire

Green Sapphire
Corundum

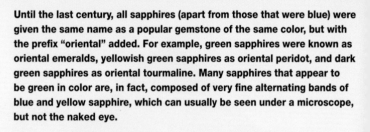

Class: oxides and hydroxides

Crystal system: trigonal

Composition: aluminum oxide

Habit: steep hexagonal bipyramids, or stout columns

Until the last century, all sapphires (apart from those that were blue) were given the same name as a popular gemstone of the same color, but with the prefix "oriental" added. For example, green sapphires were known as oriental emeralds, yellowish green sapphires as oriental peridot, and dark green sapphires as oriental tourmaline. Many sapphires that appear to be green in color are, in fact, composed of very fine alternating bands of blue and yellow sapphire, which can usually be seen under a microscope, but not the naked eye.

Properties and characteristics: Green sapphires are generally yellowish, olive, or dark tourmaline green color, with green to bluish green and yellowish green pleochroism (showing different colors in different directions). The color is not as bright as that of the finest chrome tourmalines, tsavorite garnets, or emeralds; however, green sapphires can often appear very similar to these stones, and it make take some scrutiny to tell them apart. The color is the result of traces of ferrous and ferric iron.

Cutting, setting, and valuing: The very finest green sapphires come from Sri Lanka, but these are very rare. These stones are normally lighter green, and less vibrant than those found in Thailand and Australia. These latter countries produce some lovely green sapphires, but many contain impurities that give them a yellow or blue hue which decreases their beauty and value. Well-colored green sapphires that exhibit high levels of clarity and are of a good size (over 10 carats) are in relatively short supply. Mixed oval and cushion cuts are the most common, but you can sometimes find square or rectangular step cuts. Their durability makes green sapphires excellent choices for mounting in jewelry as well as including in any collection.

Refractive index:	1.761–1.780
Birefringence:	0.008
Dispersion:	0.018
Specific gravity:	3.98–4.00
Hardness:	9
Cleavage:	weak basal parting
Fracture:	conchoidal
Luster:	adamantine to vitreous
Notable locations:	Thailand, Sri Lanka, Australia, Tanzania, Montana in the USA
Color:	light to dark green

Trigonal Green sapphire

Pink Sapphire
Corundum

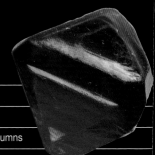

Class:	oxides and hydroxides
Crystal system:	trigonal
Composition:	aluminum oxide
Habit:	steep hexagonal bipyramids, or stout columns

Pink sapphires are a type of corundum known as fancy sapphires. They are colored by the same element as rubies—chromium—although in smaller amounts. They are not in the same league as rubies in terms of price and desirability. However, in some countries these stones are incorrectly called rubies.

Properties and characteristics: Pink sapphires are colored by small quantities of chromium impurities. Increasingly higher levels of chromium deepen the color until it becomes a ruby. Sri Lankan pink sapphires tend to have a bluish hue, making them appear almost purple. Pink sapphires also come from Burma (Myanmar), the home of many historic rubies, and there are also pink and red-orange sapphires from African deposits. Many new pink sapphires are appearing from mines in Madagascar. These gems are relative newcomers to the market, and there are many color variations. Vietnam is a significant source of pink to purple sapphires, from several deposits.

Cutting, setting, and valuing: The most popular and expensive pink sapphires have colors that are not far removed from that of rubies. Purplish stones are worth less, and pale and brownish stones are still less expensive. Like most corundum, pink sapphires are faceted in brilliant, cushion, and briolette cuts. Inclusions are common in pink sapphires, but the most expensive varieties are eye-clean (clear to the eye) unless there is asterism. A reddish or purplish-pink star stone may be accepted by experts as a star ruby, and then is worth much more.

Refractive index:	1.761–1.780
Birefringence:	0.008
Dispersion:	0.018
Specific gravity:	3.98–4.00
Hardness:	9
Cleavage:	weak basal parting
Fracture:	conchoidal
Luster:	adamantine to vitreous
Notable locations:	Sri Lanka, Vietnam, Burma (Myanmar), Tanzania, Kenya, Madgascar
Color:	shades of pink to purple-pink (magenta)

Trigonal Pink Sapphire

Yellow Sapphire
Corundum

Class: oxides and hydroxides

Crystal system: trigonal

Composition: aluminum oxide

Habit: steep hexagonal bipyramids, or stout columns

Until the 1880s, yellow sapphires were known as oriental topaz. In the majority of stones the color is a pale wheaty yellow, but it may vary through shades of green or brown; in the former case it approaches the color of yellow-green sapphire. Precious corundum with a distinctive yellow color is fairly common. Colorless sapphires are often heat treated to produce a yellow color.

Properties and characteristics: The color of yellow sapphires is due to the presence of iron in the stone. Like all members of the corundum family, yellow sapphire is found as crystals in rocks of limestone and schists (metamorphic rock), and in riverbeds and streams. However, the majority are found associated with basaltic lava flows, as in Australia, China, or Thailand. The yellow color can also be achieved by heat treatment, exposure to radiation (this color is often not light-stable), and beryllium diffusion.

Cutting, setting, and valuing: The value of this stone depends upon the particular shade of its color; orangy or pure lemon-yellow stones are the most highly prized. Transparency is also important, as is uniformity of color. Sri Lanka produces sapphires in yellow, light green, and colorless hues. Even stones with the greatest depth and intense color are less valuable than fine blue sapphires. Yellow sapphires are normally faceted as brilliants.

Refractive index:	1.761–1.780
Birefringence:	0.008
Dispersion:	0.018
Specific gravity:	3.98–4.00
Hardness:	9
Cleavage:	weak basal parting
Fracture:	conchoidal
Luster:	adamantine to vitreous
Notable locations:	Sri Lanka, India, Australia, China, Montana in the USA, Thailand
Color:	yellow, golden, orange

Trigonal Yellow Sapphire

Eudialyte

Eudialyte is a rare gemstone, first discovered in the Julianehaab district of Greenland in 1819. It derives its name from the Greek words *eu* and *dialytos*, meaning "easily decomposed," a reference to the fact that this mineral dissolves in acid. It occurs in distinctive colors of red-violet, pink, yellow, and brown. Stones with an intense carmine color are known as "dragon's blood" by some Russian dealers.

Properties and characteristics: Eudialyte is a cyclosilicate mineral. Good crystals are only rarely formed, and eudialyte only occasionally forms any crystal faces at all. It normally appears as a component of a host rock. Almandine spar is an alternative name for eudialyte, and eucolite is the name of an altered form. Major localities of eudialyte include Mont Saint-Hilaire in Quebec, Canada (stones found here typically contain fractures and veil-like heated fractures), and the Kola Peninsula in Russia (where stones contain fewer inclusions but are much darker in color). It has also been found in Greenland, Norway and Arkansas in the USA.

Cutting, setting, and valuing: Eudialyte is a moderately soft and brittle gem that requires judicious care when setting. Although masses are handsized or larger, facetable areas are small, and clear stones are typically under half a carat. Large cabochons have been fashioned from opaque material. Russian eudialyte is considered to be the most valuable. Despite its clear beauty, eudialyte remains more of a collectable curiosity than a long-lasting gemstone.

Refractive index:	1.596–1.602
Birefringence:	0.004
Dispersion:	strong
Specific gravity:	2.88
Hardness:	5–6
Cleavage:	imperfect in one direction
Fracture:	uneven
Luster:	vitreous
Notable locations:	Sweden, Canada (Sheffield Lake and Mont Saint-Hilaire, Quebec), Russia (Kola Peninsula), Greenland
Color:	dark to medium red, orange-red, brownish red

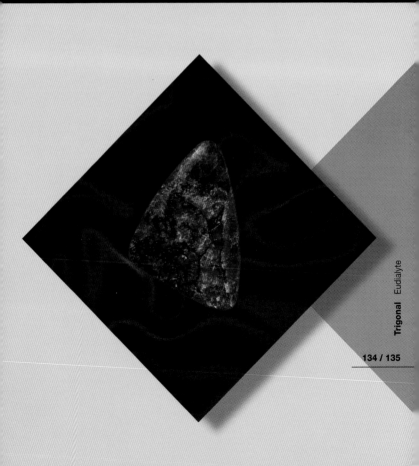

Trigonal Eudialyte

Calcite

Class: carbonates	
Crystal system: trigonal	
Composition: calcium carbonate	
Habit: many, from spiky to tabular	

Calcite gets its name from *calx*, the Latin word for "lime," and it is among the most common minerals on the earth's crust. Iceland spar is a colorless, transparent variety of calcite, which is well known for its extremely strong doubling (double refraction, or birefringence). Mexican onyx is a banded translucent variety of calcite that is widely used for ornamental purposes.

Properties and characteristics: Calcite can form very large rocks, and constitutes a noteworthy part of metamorphic and sedimentary rocks. Over 300 different crystal forms have been identified in calcite, and they combine to produce many thousands of crystal variations. Fluorescence, phosphorescence, thermoluminescence, and triboluminescence are other key properties of calcite, but not every specimen will have them. Some spar calcite from Mexico is capable of fluorescing in a beautiful blue or violet shade, and some specimens phosphoresce (maintain their glow) after the source of light has been removed.

Cutting, setting, and valuing: Calcite is very low on the hardness scale, and it is not sought as a gem-quality mineral since it is prone to scratch; however, it is still used as cabochons, faceted cuts, and carvings in the gem industry. A white, fibrous variety of calcite can be cut en cabochon to show a chatoyant effect. Fine specimens of calcite are easy to obtain and inexpensive, because they are so naturally abundant. Beautiful colorless crystals have been found in Michigan in the USA, Russia, India, and elsewhere in the world. Collectors prize giant, faceted, transparent, colorless calcites for the colored flashes produced due to the stone's high birefringence.

Refractive index:	1.486–1.658
Birefringence:	0.172
Dispersion:	0.02
Specific gravity:	2.71
Hardness:	3
Cleavage:	perfect in three directions
Fracture:	uneven
Luster:	vitreous to pearly
Notable locations:	England, Mexico, India, Iceland; New York, Montana, and Utah in the USA; Namibia, Russia
Color:	white, yellow, brown, pink, blue etc.

Trigonal Calcite

Class: silicates (silicates with isolated silica units)	
Crystal system: trigonal	
Composition: beryllium silicate	
Habit: usually flattened rhombohedra	

Phenakite is a rare beryllium silicate mineral that has been used as a gemstone, and is often noted for its high refractive index. It is also known as phenacite. The name phenakite is derived from the Greek word *phenax*, meaning "deceiver," which alludes to the fact that this mineral is often mistaken for quartz. Despite its rarity, it is commonly found with other precious gemstones. In some cases, phenakite is entirely colorless and transparent, but it tends to be clouded and milky in most specimens. In some cases, it has a pinkish or yellow tinge.

Properties and characteristics: Phenakite is found in pegmatitic pockets (vugs), granitic igneous rocks, and hydrothermal veins. It also occurs in schists alongside beryl. Phenakite is also very often found with other gemstones, such as topaz, cassiterite, calcite, beryl (especially emerald), chrysoberyl, and smoky quartz. Its crystal system is trigonal, and it often crystallizes in short prisms. Phenakite can vary greatly in form from one location to another. The Ural Mountains in Russia have produced excellent stones, particularly near Ekaterinburg, and good specimens have also been uncovered in Brazil. Phenakite is commonly found as an inclusion in some synthetic emeralds.

Cutting, setting, and valuing: High-quality crystals of phenakite are often perfectly clear. Their good hardness, rarity, and lack of good cleavage make them excellent choices for gemstones, although they are not often used for this purpose. The crystals are somewhat lacking in color and fire, but they have a frosted appearance; when they are properly cut, they produce lovely gems, with a unique luster. Phenakite is normally faceted in a mixed or brilliant cut. It is quite popular with collectors, particularly in its twinned crystal forms.

Refractive index:	1.651–1.670
Birefringence:	0.016
Dispersion:	0.015
Specific gravity:	2.92–2.97
Hardness:	7.5–8
Cleavage:	distinct in one direction
Fracture:	conchoidal
Luster:	vitreous
Notable locations:	Russia, Brazil, Sri Lanka, Austria, Switzerland, France, Namibia, Tanzania
Color:	colorless; also may be yellow, pink, or brown due to surface stains

Trigonal Phenakite

Dioptase

Class: silicates (ring silicates)

Crystal system: trigonal

Composition: hydrated copper silicate

Habit: prisms or rhombohedral crystals

Dioptase is an extraordinarily beautiful mineral, and its spirited green color makes it one of the few gems that can compare with the emerald, for which it was first mistaken. It is quite soft, with a good cleavage, so it is not usually cut as a gemstone. Dioptase was given its name by French mineralogist Rene Just Haüy in 1797, after the Greek words *dia*, meaning "through" and *optizein*, meaning "to see," an allusion to the two cleavage directions that are apparent inside crystals that are unbroken.

Property and characteristics: Dioptase is very rare, and usually mined in arid desert regions, where it forms as a secondary mineral in copper sulfide mineral deposits (hence the green coloring). Many crystals are clear, but their rich coloration can make them appear cloudy. Dioptase crystallizes in the trigonal system and most commonly occurs as prismatic to rhombohedral crystals, which can reach 2 in (5 cm) in some places. Some localities produce elongated prisms. The mineral also occurs in crystalline crusts (druses) and finely crystalline aggregates.

Cutting, setting, and valuing: Fine crystals of dioptase are available from Russia, but certain important African sources are no longer active. Larger crystals are rare. Dioptase is rarely faceted (and then only for a collector, since the stones are too soft and brittle to be cut as jewelry); when it is faceted, the brilliant cut is generally used. Cabochon cuts and beads are more common.

Refractive index:	1.644–1.709
Birefringence:	0.053
Dispersion:	0.036
Specific gravity:	3.28–3.35
Hardness:	5
Cleavage:	perfect in three directions
Fracture:	conchoidal
Luster:	vitreous
Notable locations:	Russia, Zaire, Chile, Namibia, USA
Color:	emerald green, bluish green

Trigonal Dioptase

Class: carbonates

Crystal system: trigonal

Composition: calcium magnesium carbonate

Habit: rhombohedra and saddle-shaped
intergrowths

Dolomite comprises the chief source of magnesium acquired from the crust of the earth. It is a sedimentary rock-forming mineral, and is usually mined from massive beds that can reach several hundred feet in depth. This brittle stone consists of calcium magnesium carbonate. Dolomite was first described in 1797 by French naturalist and geologist Deodat de Gratet de Dolomieu (1750–1801), from its occurrence in a region of the Italian Alps (now called the Dolomites in his honor). Dolomite can be several different colors, but colorless and white are most common. The luster of dolomite is probably one of the best examples of a pearly luster.

Properties and characteristics: Pure dolomite may appear either white or yellow. Small amounts of iron in the composition give the crystals a yellow to brown tint; a high manganese content can make the crystals a pale rose-pink; and cobalt turns it a more purplish pink. Dolomite looks very much like calcite, which consists only of calcium carbonate. It forms white, gray to pink, and mainly curved crystals, although the habit is normally massive. Its physical properties are similar to those of calcite.

Cutting, setting, and valuing: Crystals of dolomite from the Midwest USA are well known for their beautiful pink color, pearly luster, and unusual crystal habit. Colorless dolomite is rarely faceted because of its softness and perfect cleavage, although some crystals are cut for collectors—usually in a step cut.

Refractive index:	1.502–1.681
Birefringence:	0.179
Dispersion:	0.027
Specific gravity:	2.8–2.9
Hardness:	3.5–4
Cleavage:	perfect in three directions
Fracture:	subconchoidal
Luster:	vitreous to pearly
Notable locations:	Midwest USA, Ontario, Canada, Switzerland, Spain, Mexico
Color:	white, gray to pink

Trigonal Dolomite

Smithsonite

Class: carbonates

Crystal system: trigonal

Composition: zinc carbonate

Habit: usually in curved masses, but sometimes rhombohedral

Smithsonite is a zinc carbonate mineral. It was named after James Smithson (1765–1829), a British mineralogist and chemist who left a bequest in his will to found the Smithsonian Institute in the USA. Smithson first distinguished the mineral from calamine (hemimorphite). However, two millennia ago, Romans extracted zinc from smithsonite and mixed it with copper to make brass.

Properties and characteristics: Smithsonite is a rare carbonate, and is most often found with the minerals galena and sphalerite, especially in regions rich in limestone. Like dolomite, it has a unique, pearly luster, in this case resembling glowing, melted wax. Smithsonite is found as colorful botryoidal (appearing like bunches of grapes) encrustations and masses at the Kelly Mine in New Mexico, and thick yellow-banded crusts in lead mines in Marion Co., Arkansas, and many colorful stones can be found in Laurium, in Greece. A colorless and transparent variety has been mined at the Broken Hill mine in Zambia. Smithsonite's wide range of colors is the result of a number of different minor elements: Copper is responsible for green to blue colors; cobalt gives the pink to purple colors; cadmium produces yellowish colors; and iron oxide inclusions make brown to red colors.

Cutting, setting, and valuing: Most smithsonite is found in soft layers or in masses, and these are used as ornamental stones, usually cut en cabochon. Some crystals can be found (colorless ones in Zambia, for example), and these are faceted for collectors only. The most common color is apple- to bluish-green; however, purple to lavender smithsonite is the most expensive and sought after. Smithsonite is rare, but not overly expensive, making it a popular collectors' piece.

Refractive index:	1.621–1.849
Birefringence:	0.228
Dispersion:	0.037
Specific gravity:	4.3
Hardness:	5
Cleavage:	perfect in three directions
Fracture:	uneven
Luster:	pearly to resinous
Notable locations:	Tsumeb in Namibia, Zambia, New Mexico, Arkansas, Arizona in the USA, Spain, Greece, Mexico
Color:	apple green, blue-green, lavender, purple, yellow, and colorless

Trigonal Smithsonite

Rhodochrosite

Class: carbonates

Crystal system: trigonal

Composition: manganese carbonate

Habit: rhombohedra or scalenohedra, also curved masses

Also known as raspberry spar, rhodochrosite is a cousin of the mineral calcite, but where calcite has calcium, rhodochrosite has manganese. The manganese gives the mineral its traditional rosy pink color, even in its rare transparent crystals. Other color variations are the result of minor elements such as iron. The name comes from the Greek word for "rose-colored." Rhodochrosite crystals can be extremely beautiful, but they are comparatively soft and brittle and are therefore rarely fashioned as jewelry for everyday use.

Properties and characteristics: Individual crystals are found in nicely shaped rhombohedra and, less commonly, scalenohedra (crystals with a distinctive tooth-shape). In its massive form, the pink and white bands are stunningly beautiful, and are regularly used to fashion semiprecious jewelry. Some calcites and dolomites with a small amount of manganese or cobalt can also be pink in color.

Cutting, setting, and valuing: Faceted cuts can be used for jewelry (although the mineral is too soft to be used as a ring stone), as can beads. Although clean stones have been seen, these are quite rare and definitely sought after. Most faceted rhodochrosite gems contain light to moderate inclusions. In most cases, crystals are under five carats, and any eye-clean stone (that is, a stone that is clear to the eye) over 10 carats is considered to be large. The largest top-quality faceted rhodochrosite gem weighs over 90 carats. Most Argentinian rhodochrosite is opaque, and it tends to be cut or carved en cabochon. Material that is from stalactites can be cut into unusual discs with a bull's eye pattern.

Refractive index:	1.600–1.820
Birefringence:	0.220
Dispersion:	about 0.025
Specific gravity:	3.50–3.65
Hardness:	4
Cleavage:	perfect in three directions
Fracture:	uneven
Luster:	vitreous to pearly
Notable locations:	Argentina, Colorado in the USA, South Africa, Peru, Romania, Hungary, Canada
Color:	banded: pink, white, gray, brown; transparent: pink, red, orange-red

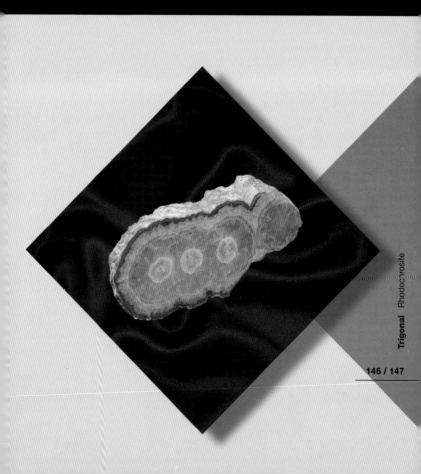

Trigonal Rhodochrosite

Rubellite
Elbaite or Liddicoatite Tourmaline

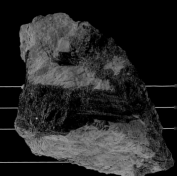

Class: silicates (ring silicates)

Crystal system: trigonal

Composition: complex borosilicate

Habit: prisms with flattened terminations, often striated vertically

Rubellite is a variety of elbaite or liddicoatite tourmaline, which can occur in any color; in the case of rubellite, the color ranges from light pink to deep red. The name rubellite (*Rubellit* in German, and *rubellita* in Spanish) is derived from the Latin name *rubellus*, meaning "reddish." This is, of course, a reference to its distinct color.

Properties and characteristics: Rubellite is a complex crystalline silicate (cyclosilicate, or ring silicate) containing aluminum, boron, and minor amounts of manganese and iron. It is also rich in lithium. Rubellite usually occurs in hexagonal, prismatic crystals, which tend to be elongated and vertically striated. The crystals can grow up to 3 feet (1 meter) in length. It forms in igneous and metamorphic rocks; it is best developed in pegmatites, rather than in high-temperature veins. Rubellite is strongly piezoelectric (see page 154) and it is also pyroelectric, meaning that it becomes electrically charged when it is heated. Rubellite fractures easily across the crystal. The specific gravity varies with the color; for example, deep red rubellite has a higher specific gravity than pale pink or even lighter reds.

Cutting, setting, and valuing: Most faceted rubellite available has probably been heat treated and/or irradiated to improve its color. Usual cuts include briolettes, step cuts, and cabochon. Rubellite tourmalines should be eye clean; large, good-quality stones have a high value.

Refractive index:	1.622–1.641
Birefringence:	0.019
Dispersion:	0.017
Specific gravity:	3.03–3.05
Hardness:	7–7.5
Cleavage:	none
Fracture:	uneven to subconchoidal
Luster:	vitreous
Notable locations:	Brazil, Madagascar, Mozambique, Nigeria, Pakistan, Russia
Color:	pale pink through to deep red/purple

Trigonal Rubellite

Indicolite
Elbaite or Liddicoatite Tourmaline

Class: silicates (ring silicates)

Crystal system: trigonal

Composition: complex borosilicate

Habit: prisms with flattened terminations,
      sometimes needle-shaped or fibrous

**Indicolite is the blue variety of the tourmaline minerals elbaite and
liddicoatite. It derives its name from the Latin for the indicum (indigo)
plant, famed for its opulent blue colors. It is commonly found in North
America, Madagascar, Brazil, Namibia, Africa, Australia, and Sri Lanka.**

Properties and characteristics: Indicolite is pleochroic, meaning it can show
different colors (or lighter and darker tones) when viewed from different angles.
It is transparent to opaque and is found in igneous and metamorphic rocks,
and best developed in pegmatites. A true indicolite will be pure blue, but most
range from light greenish blue, through to bright blue, and up to rich, dark blue.
Although some material is very clean, indicolite typically contains hollow tube
inclusions, and cat's eyes are not uncommon.

Cutting, setting, and valuing: Like all tourmalines, indicolite can be
beautifully set, and it wears well in almost any type of jewelry. Step cuts are
most common. Buyers need to ensure that the color is correct: Indicolite
should be a light to dark, very saturated blue; many gems sold on the market
are not true indicolites. Small stones (between one and eight carats) are
common, and stones up to even 15 carats are available. Larger stones tend
to be collectors' items, but excellent stones that are up to 100 carats in weight
are not unheard of.

Refractive index:	1.622–1.641
Birefringence:	0.019
Dispersion:	0.017
Specific gravity:	3.05–3.11
Hardness:	7–7.5
Cleavage:	imperfect
Fracture:	uneven to subconchoidal
Luster:	vitreous
Notable locations:	Brazil, Madagascar, Namibia, USA, Africa, Australia, Sri Lanka
Color:	light green-blue through to deep blue

Trigonal Indicolite

Dravite
Tourmaline

Class: silicates (ring silicates)

Crystal system: trigonal

Composition: complex borosilicate

Habit: usually equant prisms with pyramids, can look like garnet crystals

In 1883, the Austrian scientist Tschermak described a previously unknown brown mineral of the tourmaline mineral group. He named the mineral dravit because of its close proximity to the Drau (Drava) River in Austria. It is a magnesian mineral in the tourmaline family, which occurs in pegmatites and granites, and also in some metamorphic rock. Dark varieties are often mistaken for schorl, and small specimens could be mistaken for buergerite, both of which are other tourmaline minerals.

Properties and characteristics: Dravite forms in rare conditions, in light to dark brown crystals with well-developed, small prismatic and pyramid planes that are rarely bigger than ¾ in (2 cm). The biggest dravite found was about 4 in (10 cm) long. Dravite can be confused with brown garnets, but close examination of the mineral should reveal its trigonal shape, and the characteristic triangular face at each end of the crystal. The stone can be lightened by heat treatment.

Cutting, setting, and valuing: Because it displays a strong dichroism, dravite should be cut with the tablet facet parallel to the length of the crystal, encouraging a lighter, more appealing color. Brilliant and cushion cuts are common. Tourmalines are popular stones, and price is often dependent upon color and transparency. Because dravite is brown, often opaque, and fairly common, it has lower gem value than many stones.

Refractive index:	1.612–1.661
Birefringence:	0.022–0.029
Dispersion:	0.017
Specific gravity:	3.06–3.40
Hardness:	7–7.5
Cleavage:	indistinct
Fracture:	uneven to conchoidal
Luster:	vitreous
Notable locations:	Brazil, Sri Lanka, USA, Canada, Mexico, Australia
Color:	light to dark brown; green chromdravite is related

Trigonal Dravite

Achroite
Elbaite or Rossmanite Tourmaline

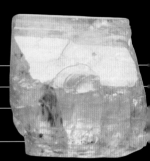

Class: silicates (ring silicates)

Crystal system: trigonal

Composition: complex borosilicate

Habit: prisms with flattened terminations, often striated vertically

Achroite is a rare, colorless variety of tourmaline. It is most often either the species elbaite or rossmanite, which are members of the tourmaline group. All of the minerals in the tourmaline group are isomorphous, and share very similar physical characteristics. Tourmaline come in many colors, from the colorless achroite to schorl and other black species. Elbaite is a separate species of the tourmaline group, and its color varies greatly; the species rossmanite is usually colorless. Achroite is named after the Greek word *achroos*, meaning "without color."

Properties and characteristics: The colorless form of tourmaline is very rare. Very light pink tourmaline can be made colorless by heat treatment; however, this process causes the crystals to become more brittle and the facet junctions likelier to grind down. The most common occurrence of achroite is in granite pegmatites (the large-grained last crystallizing part of granite). Like all of the tourmalines, achroite collects electrical charges at either end of a crystal when it is heated. If an electrical current is applied to an achroite crystal, it will vibrate—something known as the piezoelectric effect.

Cutting, setting, and valuing: This stone is not often used on its own in jewelry, but when cut correctly achroite produces beautiful gems. Achroite differs slightly from other tourmaline varieties, in that a tablet facet can be cut either parallel or perpendicular to the length of the crystal. Brilliant and mixed cuts are common. Achroite can sometimes be found with a spot of color surrounded by the clear material.

Refractive index:	1.622–1.645
Birefringence:	0.013–0.024 (probably the low part of this range)
Dispersion:	0.017
Specific gravity:	about 3.05
Hardness:	7-7.5
Cleavage:	poor, indistinct
Fracture:	uneven to subconchoidal
Luster:	vitreous
Notable locations:	Madagascar, Cornwall in the UK, Elba in Italy, Brazil, and Pala in California in the USA
Color:	colorless

Watermelon Tourmaline
Elbaite or Liddicoatite

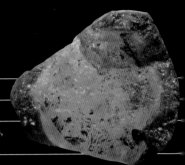

Class: silicates (ring silicates)

Crystal system: trigonal

Composition: complex borosilicate

Habit: prisms with flattened terminations, often striated vertically

This unusual-looking stone is a variety of tourmaline (usually elbaite and/or liddicoatite) with unique color zoning representing a watermelon— primarily a pink core ("the flesh") with a green outer edge ("the rind"). The concentric bands of color range from reddish, pink, or purple in the center, sometimes with a whitish zone surrounding, and then an olive-green external "rind" area. Watermelon tourmaline is most commonly found in Brazil and Madagascar.

Properties and characteristics: Watermelon tourmalines are rich in lithium, with traces of manganese and iron causing the pink and green colors, respectively. The crystals from pegmatites are often cracked or broken. A vast pocket of some of the finest watermelon crystals ever uncovered was found in the early 1970s at the Plumbago Gem Mine in Newry, Maine, USA. The colors of watermelon tourmaline occur naturally.

Cutting, setting, and valuing: These distinctive gems are highly sought by collectors. They are available in many shapes, including cross sections or slices; the most highly prized gems—and therefore the most expensive—are large with strong colors. In faceted stones, emerald cuts are particularly popular for stones with a number of hues, because the length of the gem allows the soft pastel color shifts to be seen more clearly. Rough pieces are almost as beautiful as finished, cut stones.

Refractive index:	1.622–1.641
Birefringence:	0.019
Dispersion:	0.017
Specific gravity:	3.03–3.08
Hardness:	7–7.5
Cleavage:	imperfect
Fracture:	uneven to subconchoidal
Luster:	vitreous
Notable locations:	Brazil, Madagascar, USA
Color:	zoned with a pink core, green edges, and occasionally a white band between them

Trigonal Watermelon Tourmaline

Schorl
Tourmaline

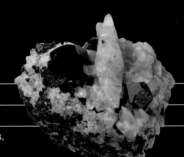

Class: silicates (ring silicates)

Crystal system: trigonal

Composition: complex borosilicate

Habit: prisms with flattened terminations, often striated vertically

Rich in iron, schorl is one of the most common members of the tourmaline family. It is named after a village in Saxony, Germany, because a great deal of black tourmaline was found in a nearby tin mine. The first descriptions of this mineral hark back to the fifteenth century, but it was during the Victorian era that schorl came into its own, being used predominantly in mourning jewelry. Schorl has now been discovered on seven continents.

Properties and characteristics: Schorl can be a major component of igneous and metamorphic rocks. Too opaque to be an attractive gemstone, schorl is often used as an ornamental stone. Some schorl crystals reach great sizes and show a wide variety of crystal faces. Long and thin crystals are common in quartz, creating the stone known as tourmalinated quartz, but this material may instead contain green elbaite needles.

Cutting, setting, and valuing: A common mineral, it has little if any value in the gem market today, despite being popular in Victorian England. In fact, the word schorl is an old German mining phrase that meant "unwanted material." It can be cut as a brilliant or with mixed facets, but this is unusual. However, because black opaque materials have had a resurgence in popularity, and because it can be polished to a high sheen (distinguishing it from black stones such as jet, onyx, and obsidian), schorl is becoming slightly more popular in the gemstone market.

Refractive Index:	1.635–1.672
Birefringence:	0.025
Dispersion:	0.015–0.020
Specific gravity:	3.15–3.22
Hardness:	7–7.5
Cleavage:	indistinct
Fracture:	conchoidal
Luster:	vitreous to resinous
Notable locations:	Brazil, Pakistan, Namibia, many others
Color:	black

Trigonal Schorl

Paraíba Tourmaline
Elbaite

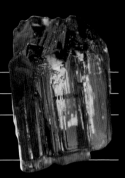

Class: silicates (ring silicates)

Crystal system: trigonal

Composition: complex borosilicate

Habit: crystals rarely preserved; sometimes seen as purple-cored blue-violet watermelon prisms in matrix

Paraíba (elbaite) tourmaline was discovered in Paraíba, Brazil, in 1989 by Heitor Dimas Barbosa. It has a unique glow that has been described as being "neon" or "electric." The color comes from copper (which had not been seen in any other tourmaline), and manganese. The interplay between these elements produces an extravagant range of rich blue, turquoise, and purple. Pale gray and violet-blue material has also been found. Subsequent discoveries of copper-bearing (cuprian) elbaite were made in Mozambique and Nigeria. Nigerian "paraiba" is paler—normally shades of aqua, mint, and pastel greeny blues. The greatest variety of colors come from Mozambique, where fuchsias, deep violets, rich blues, teals, and apple greens are common.

Properties and characteristics: These are rare, extremely sought-after stones in an array of vibrant colors unmatched in any other transparent gemstone. The most beautiful and highly valued colors (vibrant turquoise, green, and blue) are the result of high concentrations of copper, while manganese creates the beautiful shades of violet and red. Large crystals were rare at the original source in Brazil; however, "paraiba" gems produced in Africa tend to be larger. A number of stones over five carats have been found in various localities in Africa, where 50-carat stones are known.

Cutting, setting, and valuing: Almost all greenish blue examples are heat treated to remove violet tones. The vivid coloration of the Brazilian Paraíba is not evident until the stone has been faceted; it then appears to glow in even the weakest light. The Paraíba site is now almost exhausted, and excavation is tricky, mainly undertaken by hand, making these stones extremely expensive and quite rare. Five-figure-per-carat prices are not unusual for fine specimens.

Refractive index:	1.622–1.641
Birefringence:	0.019
Dispersion:	0.017
Specific gravity:	about 3.05
Hardness:	7.5
Cleavage:	imperfect
Fracture:	uneven to subconchoidal
Luster:	vitreous
Notable locations:	Mina da Batalha in Paraíba, and two mines in Rio Grande do Norte, Brazil; similar tourmalines found in Nigeria and Mozambique
Color:	emerald green through to turquoise, sky blue, neon blue, indigo, and purple

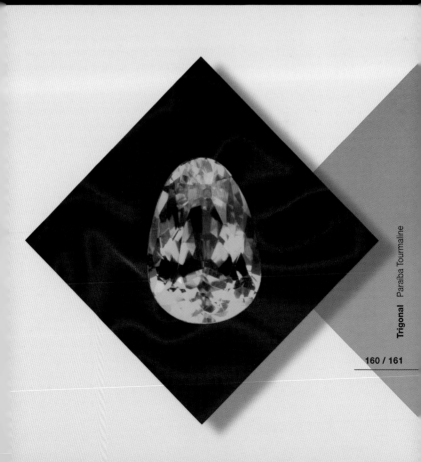

Trigonal Paraíba Tourmaline

Aragonite

Class: carbonates

Crystal system: orthorhombic

Composition: calcium carbonate

Habit: needlelike crystals, layered crusts, or twins looking like hexagonal columns

Aragonite is a carbonate mineral with the same chemical composition as calcite, making it a polymorph of that mineral. The Spanish region of Aragon is where aragonite was first discovered, and from where it gets its name. Aragonite crystals are slim and tapering, but it can also form columnar masses, stalactites, and crusts. Normally white, colorless, or honey-colored, aragonite is common and can be found worldwide. Some specimens have been known to fluoresce green. Aragonite that contains small amounts of copper forms slightly greenish to bluish masses.

Properties and characteristics: The chemical name for aragonite is calcium carbonate, but it may also contain strontium, lead, or zinc within its structure. It is usually deposited in regions around hot springs, and is found in sedimentary rocks, and in various ore veins. Aragonite is also the main mineral that makes up the inorganic framework of mother of pearl (see page 278). An aragonite cave, the Ochtinská Aragonite Cave, is situated in Slovakia. In the USA, stalactitic aragonite has been found in many caves in Bisbee, Arizona. Massive deposits of oolitic aragonite are found on the floor of the sea in the Bahamas.

Cutting, setting, and valuing: Tumbled, polished stones, and beads are the most common cuts; this stone is also used widely in carvings, sculpture, lamps, and ornaments. Rarely, transparent colorless or light brown aragonite is faceted for collectors.

Refractive index:	1.530–1.685
Birefringence:	0.155
Dispersion:	0.226
Specific gravity:	2.93–2.95
Hardness:	3.5–4
Cleavage:	distinct in one direction
Fracture:	subconchoidal
Luster:	vitreous
Notable locations:	Aragon in Spain, Morocco, France, England, Scotland, California in the USA, Germany, Mexico, Slovakia
Color:	white or colorless; often very pale shades of red, yellow, orange, brown, green, and blue

Orthorhombic Aragonite

Barite

Class: sulfates

Crystal system: orthorhombic

Composition: barium sulfate

Habit: many shapes, from tabular to prismatic; also "roses"

Barite (which is also spelled baryte and sometimes known as heavy spar) derives its name from the Greek word *barys*, meaning "heavy," which refers to its high specific gravity. Barite is the mineral name for barium sulfate, a mineral that was considered worthless until, during the Middle Ages, it was discovered that some samples that had been heat treated became luminescent; these were subsequently known as "phosphoric stones of Bologna."

Properties and characteristics: Natural barite is found as tabular crystals or in granular or massive forms. The mineral is widely distributed throughout the world, often occurring in veins with lead and zinc minerals. The bladed or tabular crystals of barite often form a pattern of concentric circles radiating outwards. This occurrence gives the crystal the appearance of a flower. When colored red by iron stains, these formations are known as "desert roses." Crystals vary from being completely opaque to transparent. Barite is sometimes fluorescent under UV light.

Cutting, setting, and valuing: Barite is a common mineral, yet it yields some very striking specimens. It is often used as an accessory mineral to other minerals and can create an attractive backdrop for brightly colored crystals. Not only is barite soft and brittle, but it has a high density and two perfect cleavages, all of which make it inappropriate for jewelry. Although gem-quality crystals can be found, the mineral is generally cut for collectors only. It is usually faceted in a step or mixed cut, or polished as a stone. Barite is very popular among mineral collectors and fine specimens are greatly sought after.

Refractive index:	1.636–1.648
Birefringence:	0.012
Dispersion:	0.016
Specific gravity:	4.3–4.6
Hardness:	3
Cleavage:	perfect in two directions
Fracture:	uneven
Luster:	vitreous to pearly
Notable locations:	Oklahoma, Connecticut, and Colorado in the USA, Germany, Russia, England, Sardinia, Italy, Morocco
Color:	white or colorless, sometimes greenish, yellowish, red, blue, tawny

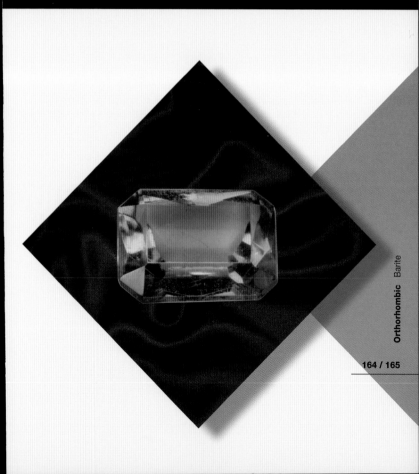

Class: sulfates

Crystal system: orthorhombic

Composition: strontium sulfate

Habit: tabular to prismatic crystals

The name celestine is derived from the Greek word *coelestis*, meaning "celestial," a reference to the pale, sky-blue shade of many of its crystals. The mineral is also known as celestite. The first celestine was discovered in 1791 near Frankstown, Pennsylvania, and described by the German mineralogist A. G. Werner. The color of blue celestine is attributed to the presence of tiny traces of potassium and to naturally occurring irradiation.

Properties and characteristics: Celestine crystals may be either tabular or prismatic (similar to barite), and fibrous forms of this mineral may also be found. Very pale blue crystal specimens are found in many places, notably in caves (geodes) in Madagascar. The largest known crystals are in a geode on the island of Put-in-Bay in Lake Erie; these can be as wide as 18 in (45 cm), and can weigh up to 300 lb (136 kg).

Cutting, setting, and valuing: Celestine is undoubtedly a favorite among mineral collectors. Blue celestine along with bright yellow sulfur is one of the most celebrated and colorful combinations of minerals available, and produces some dramatic specimens. Because of its perfect cleavage, softness, and fragility, celestine is cut only for collectors, usually in brilliant or mixed facet cuts.

Refractive index:	1.619–1.635
Birefringence:	0.010–0.012
Dispersion:	0.014
Specific gravity:	3.97–4.00
Hardness:	3.5
Cleavage:	perfect in two directions
Fracture:	uneven
Luster:	vitreous to pearly
Notable locations:	Tsumeb, Namibia; Lake Erie region of Ohio, Michigan, and New York in the USA; Madagascar, Sicily, Germany
Color:	colorless through to blue; yellow, orange, red, and red-brown more rarely

Orthorhombic Celestine

Cerussite

Class: carbonates

Crystal system: orthorhombic

Composition: lead carbonate

Habit: tabular, equant, bipyramidal; also "snowflake" twins

Cerussite is an admired collector's stone, also known as lead spar. The name cerussite is from the Latin *cerussa*, meaning "white lead." There are, however, a number of color variations as the result of inclusions. For example, black and gray crystals contain inclusions of galena (lead sulfide), and green crystals derive their color from malachite. Chrome cerussite contains the element chromium and is bright yellow. Cerussite is the most plentiful secondary lead mineral at Tsumeb mines in Namibia.

Properties and characteristics: Cerussite is a lead carbonate mineral, and it is usually found in the oxidized zones of lead ore deposits. It is transparent to opaque and very brittle. Cerussite is formed by the action of carbonate and bicarbonate solutions on galena (a lustrous, blue-gray, lead-ore mineral). Cerussite has been known to form some intricate geometrical constructions and interesting star shapes as a result of the multiple twinning that occurs in its crystal structure. It is an important ore of lead, and it is widely distributed throughout the world. Its high luster is mainly the result of its high lead content. For a transparent mineral, cerussite is extremely and unusually dense.

Cutting, setting, and valuing: Cerussite is a popular mineral, known for its high density and excellent sparkle. Cerussite twins are an essential gem for collectors of twinned crystals. Its softness makes it inappropriate for use as a gemstone, but it is frequently faceted in a brilliant cut for collectors. The best transparent and colorless crystals have come from Tsumeb in Namibia, and here, excellent, clear, twinned crystals have been found up to 23 in (60 cm) in length. Most crystals are twinned but a few untwinned specimens are seen from time to time. The largest cut cerussite weighs about 900 carats and is at the Royal Ontario Museum in Toronto, Canada.

Refractive index:	1.804–2.078
Birefringence:	0.274
Dispersion:	0.055
Specific gravity:	6.46–6.57
Hardness:	3.5
Cleavage:	distinct in two directions
Fracture:	conchoidal
Luster:	adamantine to waxy
Notable locations:	Tsumeb in Namibia, Congo, Morocco, Australia, Germany, Tasmania; and Utah, New Mexico, and Arizona in the USA
Color:	colorless or white; also gray, yellow, blue-green, black

Orthorhombic Cerussite

Topaz

Class: silicates (silicates with isolated silica units)

Crystal system: orthorhombic

Composition: aluminum silicate fluoride and/or hydroxide

Habit: long prisms, usually with chisel-shaped tips; also short prisms

Topaz has been used in jewelry for hundreds of years. Naturally golden brown to yellow, it is sometimes confused with the less valuable citrine. The name is derived from the Greek *topazios*, the early name of St. John's Island in the Red Sea, where a yellow stone was mined in ancient times. That stone is now believed to have been chrysolite or olivine. Alternatively, the name may have come from the Sanskrit *tapas*, meaning "fire." The blue color of gem topaz is usually unnatural and often produced by irradiating and then heating clear crystals.

Properties and characteristics: Topaz occurs in igneous rocks, and it may also be found as pebbles in sediments deposited by streams or rivers. When it is heated, yellow topaz often becomes orangy pink (although the color of some pink topaz is natural). Pink and red topaz are the result of chromium replacing aluminum in its structure, while orange varieties are caused by chromium and color centers; blue, yellow, and brown topazes all contain color centers. Topaz is one of the hardest minerals found in the natural world, and it is the hardest of the silicate family of minerals.

Cutting, setting, and valuing: This is a durable, beautiful gemstone, perfect for jewelry. It is faceted in brilliant, cushion, briolette, step, and mixed cuts, as well as cut en cabochon, and beads. Modern cutters make exquisite carvings and intaglios in topaz. Imperial topaz is a rich orangish yellow to orange-brown type of topaz, and, is its most valuable gem form. Natural pinks, purples, and bicolor topazes are also valuable. Gem crystals and cut stones may be incredibly large: an 18-in (45-cm) tall crystal at the Smithsonian weighs 111 lbs (50 kg). Collectors will pay premiums for crystals, particularly those in a matrix.

Refractive index:	1.609–1.637
Birefringence:	0.008–0.010
Dispersion:	0.014
Specific gravity:	3.52–3.56
Hardness:	8
Cleavage:	perfect in one direction
Fracture:	subconchoidal to uneven
Luster:	vitreous
Notable locations:	Pakistan, Mexico, Ukraine, Ouro Preto in Brazil, Ural Mountains in Russia, San Diego Co., California and the Thomas Range, Utah in the USA.
Color:	colorless, yellow, orange, red, blue, and green

Orthorhombic Topaz

Chrysoberyl

Class: oxides and hydroxides

Crystal system: orthorhombic

Composition: beryllium aluminum oxide

Habit: tabular or short prismatic with lengthwise striations; twinned hexagons

The name chrysoberyl comes from the Greek words *chryso*, meaning "golden" and *beryl*, the word for "green gemstone." It is not actually a beryl, but an unrelated gem mineral. Alexandrite is a rare variety of chrysoberyl that changes color depending on the type of light that reaches it (the change-of-color phenomenon, which should not be confused with pleochroism). In sunlight and similar fluorescent light, it appears almost emerald green, while in incandescent and "warm" fluorescent light it appears violet-red. The term cat's eye, when used without a modifier, refers to chrysoberyl cat's eye.

Properties and characteristics: Chrysoberyls are beryllium aluminum oxide. Gems without a special variety name come in many shades between lemon to honey or soft brownish green; the color is caused by the presence of iron and/or vanadium. They are mostly found in gemstone deposits in Brazil, Sri Lanka, and Tanzania. Chrysoberyl usually occurs in granite rocks, pegmatites, and schists. It has also been found in contact metamorphic deposits of dolomite marble, alongside corundum, and in fluorine skarns. Most chrysoberyl is retrieved from river sands and gravels. A special feature of uncut chrysoberyl crystals are the cyclic twins known as trillings—that is, three combined crystals, in a hexagonal prism form.

Cutting, setting, and valuing: Chrysoberyl cat's eyes are genuinely rare. All chrysoberyl is valuable and greatly sought after, particularly in deeper colors and larger stones. Common faceted cuts include mixed, cushion, and brilliant, and cat's eyes are cut en cabochon. Beads and carving are also popular. Alexandrites, especially those showing a strong color change, are far more valuable than other chrysoberyls, and there are even cat's eye alexandrites.

Refractive index:	1.740–1.770
Birefringence:	0.009–0.011
Dispersion:	0.015
Specific gravity:	3.64–3.75
Hardness:	8.5
Cleavage:	one distinct, one imperfect
Fracture:	uneven
Luster:	vitreous
Notable locations:	Sri Lanka, India, Brazil, Madagascar, Russia, Tanzania, Zimbabwe
Color:	green, brown, yellow

Orthorhombic Chrysoberyl

Andalusite

Class: silicates (silicates with isolated silica units)

Crystal system: orthorhombic

Composition: aluminum silicate

Habit: nearly square, columnar crystals, or massive

Andalusite is a pretty and unusual gemstone. It is named after Andalucia, southern Spain, where it was discovered. Many andalusites display different colors within the same stone—the result of its strong pleochroism. It is one of three polymorphs of aluminum silicate, the other two being sillimanite and kyanite. Each is formed under different pressure and temperature conditions.

Properties and characteristics: Andalusite is an aluminum silicate mineral that occurs in relatively small quantities in various metamorphic rocks, specifically in altered sediments. It is found extensively in the Inyo Mountains, Mono County, California, in the USA; in Kazakhstan, and in South Africa. Most specimens contain inclusions of some description, the most common being needles of rutile. There is a massive bright green variety called viridine (from Arizona) that is colored by manganese.

Cutting, setting, and valuing: Cuts with a long axis (in particular, oval, marquis, or emerald cuts) often show one color near the center and a second (usually darker) color towards the ends. Square and round cuts frequently blend the colors into a mosaic effect. The most common faceted cuts are brilliants and baguettes. A translucent to opaque variety of andalusite known as chiastolite contains dark inclusions in a cruciform arrangement. These are cut and polished for use as amulets in many countries, largely because of the symbolism of the cross. Despite being attractive, hard, and tough enough for high-quality jewelry, andalusite is still comparatively unknown. As a result, even clean gems with good color are not expensive; custom cuts and gems that contain exceptional inclusions tend to be more valuable.

Refractive index:	1.634–1.648
Birefringence:	0.007–0.011
Dispersion:	0.016
Specific gravity:	3.15–3.17
Hardness:	7.5
Cleavage:	distinct in one direction
Fracture:	splintery
Luster:	vitreous
Notable locations:	Sri Lanka, Spain, Brazil, Burma (Myanmar), Kazakhstan, South Africa, China, Ural Mountains in Russia, Arizona and California in the USA
Color:	brown, green, yellow are common; also pink and violet

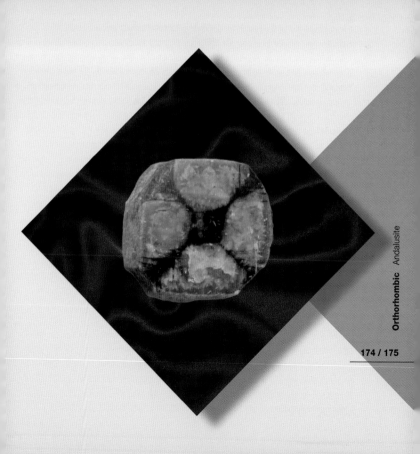

Orthorhombic Andalusite

Danburite

Class: silicates (silicates with silicate or borate tetrahedra in pairs)

Crystal system: orthorhombic

Composition: calcium borosilicate

Habit: prismatic crystals, rhombic or square in cross section

First discovered in 1839, in Danbury, Connecticut, and described by chemist and mineralogist Charles Upham Shephard (1804–1886), danburite has been found and mined in Japan, Mexico, Burma (Myanmar), and Madagascar. It ranges from colorless to light yellow, or pale pink to creamy taupe. Rare blue cat's eyes are found in Bolivia. Its toughness, poor cleavage, and hardness of seven make it an excellent jewelry stone.

Properties and characteristics: Danburite is a rare silicate mineral of calcium and boron. The crystals are similar to topaz, and danburite is an excellent example of perfectly transparent crystal clusters, making it popular with collectors. Although it looks somewhat similar to clear quartz, it has a diamond-like cross section, and wedge-shaped termination which are very different to the hexagonal prisms and pyramid-shaped terminations of quartz. Many examples of danburite fluoresce a rich sky-blue color in longwave UV light, and phosphoresce red when they are heated. Large crystals (some of them up to 4 in (10 cm) in length), have been found in conjunction with calcite in veins passing through granite, at Russell in St Lawrence County, New York. Smaller, good-quality crystals have been found at Mount Scopi and Petersthal in Switzerland. Stunning crystals have been mined in Mexico and Japan.

Cutting, setting, and valuing: Although danburite is relatively common, large, facetable pieces are rare. Danburite is also still fairly unknown in the gem world, and therefore not a major commercial jewelry stone; however, it is becoming increasingly popular with collectors. Larger, cleaner, and well-cut stones are worth the most, while colorless stones are more valuable than pastel yellow or pink ones. Stones are normally faceted in a brilliant, step, or mixed cut. Cat's eye danburites are cut en cabochon.

Refractive index:	1.630–1.636
Birefringence:	0.006
Dispersion:	0.017
Specific gravity:	3.00
Hardness:	7
Cleavage:	one poor
Fracture:	subconchoidal
Luster:	vitreous to greasy
Notable locations:	Burma (Myanmar), Japan, Madagascar, Russia, Mexico
Color:	colorless, white, pink, light to dark yellow, yellowish brown, brown

Orthorhombic Danburite

Enstatite

Class: silicates (single-chain silicates)

Crystal system: orthorhombic

Composition: magnesium silicate

Habit: prismatic, layered, or massive

The name enstatite is derived from the Greek word *enstates*, meaning "opponent," which refers to the gem's reluctance to be melted by a blowpipe, an early method for determining mineral chemistry. It was first described by German geologist G. A. Kenngott in 1855. Like hypersthene, it is a member of the pyroxene family of minerals; enstatite is a magnesium silicate.

Properties and characteristics: Enstatite is most often found in metamorphic or igneous rocks and has also been discovered in some meteorites. It forms in the orthorhombic crystal system but its structure changes to a monoclinic symmetry structure (known as clinoenstatite) at very high temperatures. Bright green enstatite (whose color is due to traces of chromium) occurs in South Africa and is known as chrome enstatite, which is cut as a gemstone. Greenish brown stones are found in upper Burma (Myanmar), and these exquisite stones often show an excellent cat's eye effect, with a thin orange to pale brown line on an almost black background. Some colorless stones and grayish cat's eye specimens are found in Sri Lanka. A deep brown, six-rayed star enstatite has been seen in Mysore, India.

Cutting, setting, and valuing: Enstatite is not well known in the world of gems and is mainly a collector's item. However, it can be found in jewelry as a cat's eye (cut en cabochon) or faceted in a step cut, usually in pendants or earrings. It is too soft for rings. Enstatite crystals with a clear crystal shape are the most rare, and therefore the most valuable.

Refractive index:	1.650–1.673
Birefringence:	0.009–0.010
Dispersion:	0.019–0.022
Specific gravity:	3.22–3.28
Hardness:	5.5
Cleavage:	distinct in two directions
Fracture:	conchoidal
Luster:	vitreous to pearly
Notable locations:	Sri Lanka, Burma (Myanmar), Tanzania, Kenya, Germany, Norway, Greenland
Color:	white, colorless, gray, brown, or green

Orthorhombic Enstatite

Sillimanite

Class: silicates (silicates with isolated silica groups)	
Crystal system: orthorhombic	
Composition: aluminum silicate	
Habit: prismatic to acicular crystals; fibrous mats	

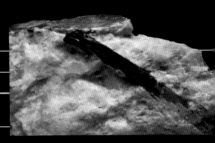

A beautiful and rare aluminosilicate mineral, sillimanite is found in two forms: One that is clear and glassy, and another that is silky and fibrous. In its fibrous state, sillimanite may be known as fibrolite. Sillimanite is named after the American geologist, Benjamin Silliman (1779–1865), a professor of chemistry and mineralogy at Yale University in the USA. The color of sillimanite varies from colorless or white through shades of gray to brown. It may also be yellowish, grayish green, or blue. It is transparent to translucent.

Properties and characteristics: Sillimanite is a mineral found in metamorphic rocks, such as gneisses, schists, or hornfels. It is only rarely found in pegmatites. It may also be found as clasts in sedimentary rocks. Sillimanite is a polymorph with two other minerals—kyanite and andalusite. A polymorph is a mineral that shares the same chemistry but a different crystal structure with another, or other, minerals. Good crystals of sillimanite are rare and most crystals have poor terminations. Sillimanite may also be found as crystal mats.

Cutting, setting, and valuing: Transparent crystals are often used as gemstones; however, gem-quality crystals are very rare, and their brittleness makes faceting difficult. Cushion cuts are most common, but are usually undertaken for collectors only. Some crystals demonstrate chatoyancy, and are cut en cabochon.

Refractive index:	1.658–1.678
Birefringence:	0.020
Dispersion:	0.015
Specific gravity:	3.14–3.28
Hardness:	7.5 (crystals), 6–7 (massive)
Cleavage:	perfect in one direction
Fracture:	splintery
Luster:	vitreous
Notable locations:	Brazil, Burma (Myanmar), Sri Lanka, Kenya, and USA
Color:	colorless, white, blue, gray, brown, and green

Orthorhombic Sillimanite

Hypersthene

Class: silicates (single-chain silicates)

Crystal system: orthorhombic

Composition: iron magnesium silicate

Habit: layered or massive; sometimes prismatic crystals

Hypersthene is a fairly common mineral, usually found in igneous and some metamorphic rocks as well as in stony and/or iron meteorites. Iron is responsible for the rich, dark color of the mineral. The name hypersthene comes from the Greek word meaning "over strength," alluding to the fact that it is harder than hornblende, a mineral with which it is often confused.

Properties and characteristics: Hypersthene usually occurs in cleavable layered masses. The color of most gem hypersthene, called bronzite, is a deep bronze color that is so opaque it almost resembles a metal. It can also be dark green, brown, or black. A rust- or copper-colored light plays over the stone, and this effect is particularly striking in good stones. Some may be cut as cat's eyes (the effect is caused by the many crystals of iron or titanium oxides that are regularly arranged in the stone). In the mid 1800s, cat's eye hypersthene came almost exclusively from the Island of Paul on the coast of Labrador, Canada.

Cutting, setting, and valuing: Vivid, eye-clean gems ranging from five to 10 carats are very rare. Stones with chatoyancy or an asterism are cut en cabochon. Tumbled, polished stones are fashionable with collectors, and the gem can be faceted, normally in the cushion or baguette cut. Hypersthene is relatively abundant in the natural world, but it is not a commonly used gemstone, making it fairly inexpensive.

Refractive index:	1.673–1.731
Birefringence:	0.010–0.016
Dispersion:	weak
Specific gravity:	3.4–3.5
Hardness:	5–6
Cleavage:	perfect in two directions
Fracture:	uneven
Luster:	vitreous to pearly
Notable locations:	Canada, New York in the USA, Mexico, Norway, Germany, South Africa
Color:	gray, brown, or green

Orthorhombic Hypersthene

Iolite
Cordierite

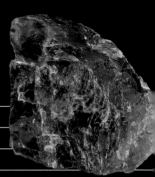

Class: silicates (ring silicates)

Crystal system: orthorhombic

Composition: magnesium aluminum silicate

Habit: usually massive, also prismatic crystals

The name iolite derives from the Greek word *ios*, meaning "violet." The stones that come from the gem gravels of Sri Lanka are sometimes called "water sapphires" because of their blue-violet color. Iolite is often known as dichroite (from the Greek, meaning "two-colored rock") because of its noticeable pleochroism: different colored light is transmitted in different directions. Iolite is the gem variety of the mineral cordierite. Centuries ago, Viking seamen used fine pieces of iolite as a polarizing filter, which was the first of its kind. They used it to determine the position of the sun, allowing them to navigate safely.

Properties and characteristics: Iolite is a blue silicate mineral that occurs as crystals or grains in igneous rocks—the result of the magma being contaminated by aluminous sediment—and more importantly in contact metamorphic rocks. This delightful, violet-blue stone is transparent to opaque, and exhibits a strong pleochroism of pale blue, deep purple-blue, and soft yellow. The major sources of gem-quality iolite come from Burma (Myanmar), Madagascar, Brazil, Sri Lanka, Tanzania, India, Namibia, and Canada. The reddish brown material, called bloodshot iolite, owes its color to reddish iron oxide inclusions.

Cutting, setting, and valuing: Color is the most important indicator of value, and the richer the blue or violet hue on the table facet of iolite, the higher its price. Iolites that are clear, colorful, well cut, and large will be less valuable if they have a yellow-brown hue. Iolite is normally faceted in step and mixed cuts, and also cut en cabochon and as beads. Although the color is attractive and the gemstone popular, it is not extremely rare and is therefore affordable.

Refractive index:	1.53–1.55
Birefringence:	0.008–0.012
Dispersion:	0.017
Specific gravity:	2.57–2.66 (all); 2.57–2.61 (gem)
Hardness:	7–7.5
Cleavage:	fair in one direction
Fracture:	subconchoidal
Luster:	vitreous
Notable locations:	Sri Lanka, India, Madagascar, Burma (Myanmar)
Color:	colorless, blue, purplish, violet blue, rarely brownish red

Orthorhombic Lolite

Kornerupine

Class: silicates (silicates with silica tetrahedral in pairs)

Crystal system: orthorhombic

Composition: hydrous magnesium aluminum borosilicate

Habit: prismatic crystals, usually incomplete in matrix

Kornerupine was discovered in Fiskernaes, Greenland, in 1887 and was named after the Danish geologist and explorer Andreas Nikolaus Kornerup (1857–1883). Most gem kornerupine is green, but non-gem kornerupine also comes in eyecatching browns, pinks and yellows.

Properties and characteristics: Kornerupine occurs in both volcanic and sedimentary rocks that contain high levels of boron, and have gone through metamorphism. It is usually found in gem gravels, and also in anorthosite complexes that have been metamorphosed. Kornerupine is extremely pleochroic (different colors can be seen from different viewing angles), and the colors change from a deep yellow-green to a brownish red when the crystal or gemstone is turned in the light. Kornerupine is often confused with beryl, peridot, topaz, or quartz, and many good stones come from Sri Lanka. Kornerupine also occasionally exhibits chatoyancy (the cat's eye effect). Madagascar currently produces kornerupine of fine colors.

Cutting, setting, and valuing: Kornerupine is most valued as a gemstone when it appears in translucent green and yellow tints. Vibrant emerald green varieties are particularly sought after, and are much harder to find. Kornerupine is not often cut for jewelry in the mainstream market, but is more of a collector's stone. When kornerupine is faceted, it is usually given a cushion or baguette cut, with the tablet facet parallel to the length of the crystal. Where there is chatoyancy, the stone is cut en cabochon.

Refractive index:	1.665–1.680
Birefringence:	0.013
Dispersion:	0.018
Specific gravity:	3.28–3.35
Hardness:	6.5
Cleavage:	one direction, indistinct
Fracture:	uneven
Luster:	vitreous
Notable locations:	Sri Lanka, Burma (Myanmar), Kenya, Tanzania, Madagascar, Canada, Nepal
Color:	green, greenish yellow, greenish brown, brownish yellow

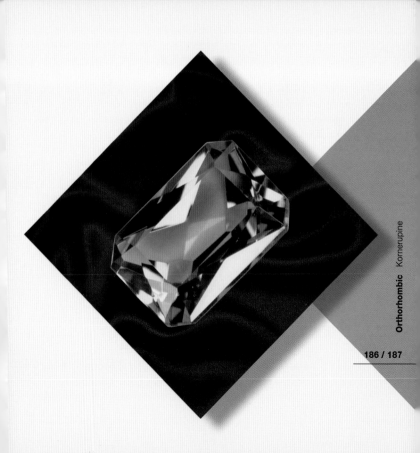

Orthorhombic Kornerupine

Peridot
Forsterite

Class: silicates (silicates with isolated silica groups)

Crystal system: orthorhombic

Composition: magnesium silicate

Habit: thick crystals with wedge-shaped terminations, or massive

Peridot was one of Cleopatra's favorite gems, and the ancient Egyptians called it the "gem of the sun," a particular point of praise as the sun was worshipped by the Egyptians. Peridot is also known as chrysolite, from the Greek for "gold stone." The name peridot may from the Greek word *peridona*, meaning "to give richness"; alternatively, it could be derived from the French word *peritot* which means "unclear," probably a reference to the inclusions that cloud the larger stones. Peridot is one of the small number of gemstones that come in just one color.

Properties and characteristics: Peridot gets its coloring from iron, which replaces about 12–15 percent of the magnesium in its structure. It is an idiochromic gem, meaning that color is due to an essential part of its composition, although the trace elements chromium and nickel make the color richer. In 1994, a new deposit was found in Pakistan, producing some of the best stones seen to date. Peridot is the gem variety of forsterite in the olivine mineral group. Its color range includes lustrous, golden lime-greens, and opulent grassy greens.

Cutting, setting, and valuing: Color is the strongest indicator of value—pure greens are the most expensive and popular; however, peridots that are slightly yellow also command high prices. In jewelry, peridot is considered to be an affordable substitute for emerald. Peridot cat's eyes and star peridot are particularly rare. Peridot is cut according to its crystal shape; it is mostly faceted in traditional table cuts, or as round, oval, or octahedron antique cuts. The smallest crystals are cut into standardized stones, while the bigger ones are used for some quite spectacular creations. Peridot is cut en cabochon if there are inclusions, to bring out their often dramatic effect.

Birefringence:	0.036
Dispersion:	0.020
Specific gravity:	3.34
Hardness:	6.5
Cleavage:	two directions, one good, one distinct
Fracture:	conchoidal
Luster:	vitreous to oily
Notable locations:	Zeberged (the Isle of St John) in Egypt, Burma (Myanmar), Pakistan, Norway; and Hawaii, California, New Mexico, and Arizona in the USA
Color:	yellowish to brownish green

Orthorhombic Peridot

Anglesite

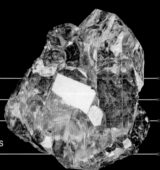

Class: sulfates

Crystal system: orthorhombic

Composition: lead sulfate

Habit: long prisms with lengthwise striations and pyramidal terminations; many others

Anglesite is an attractive and rare lead mineral. It was first recognized as a mineral species in 1783, by the English botanist, geologist, physician, and chemist, William Withering (1741–1799). He found it in the Parys copper mine in Anglesey, an island off the northwest coast of Wales. The name anglesite was coined by the French geologist and mineralogist, Francois Sulpice Beudant (1787–1850), in 1832.

Properties and characteristics: Anglesite has the same structure as barite and celestine, and forms crystals that are very similar. It is a secondary mineral that usually forms in galena (lead sulfide) ores. Anglesite occurs as prismatic orthorhombic crystals and masses. At Monteponi, in Sardinia, galena cavities are encrusted with the anglesite crystals. In Scotland, anglesites that are pseudomorphs of galena have been found. Most often, only isolated crystals are found in the lead. In some cases, as in Australia and Mexico, anglesite occurs as large masses, and it is mined as a lead ore. Some of the largest anglesite crystals were found in Tsumeb, Namibia, and excellent specimens came from Mibladen and Touissit, Morocco. Some massive anglesite specimens contain gray and black bands, which can be seen when the stone is polished or cut open. These specimens often contain unaltered galena in the center, due to the fact that when the outer layers altered to become anglesite, the center remained unaffected.

Cutting, setting, and valuing: Although anglesite is very soft, and its cleavage makes it difficult to cut, its high refractive index and dispersion produce a stunning faceted gem; it is usually faceted in a step cut. Yellow specimens are more valuable. Crystals are highly valued by collectors.

Refractive index:	1.877–1.894
Birefringence:	0.017
Dispersion:	0.044
Specific gravity:	6.30–6.39
Hardness:	3
Cleavage:	one direction good, one distinct
Fracture:	conchoidal
Luster:	adamantine
Notable locations:	Tsumeb in Namibia, Australia, Mexico, Morocco
Color:	colorless, white, and yellow; also pale gray, blue, and green

Orthorhombic Anglesite

Sinhalite

Class: carbonates (and borates)

Crystal system: orthorhombic

Composition: magnesium aluminum borate

Habit: equant crystals

Sinhalite is a rare gem, usually found in brown to greenish brown colors, although it can also be yellow. It was first discovered in Sri Lanka, where it was first believed to be a brown variety of peridot. It was identified as a mineral in 1952, when an exceptionally deep-colored specimen was found. The name sinhalite comes from the Sanskrit word *sinhala*, which was the name for the island of Ceylon (now Sri Lanka).

Properties and characteristics: Sinhalite is formed from magnesium, aluminum, boron, and oxygen; the crystals are transparent to translucent. It is found in alluvial deposits, and in gem gravels with other gemstones, such as garnet, ruby, sapphire, and peridot. It has a strong pleochroism; some specimens can appear to be different colors from green to light or dark brown when viewed from different directions. The color comes from the presence of iron. It is mined mostly in Sri Lanka, although it has also been found in Tanzania, Burma (Myanmar), Canada, USA, and Russia. Sinhalite from Sri Lanka tends to be finely pitted, the result of etching. Sinhalite is often confused with chrysoberyl, peridot, tourmaline, vesuvianite, and zircon, but its gem properties closely match those of peridot.

Cutting, setting, and valuing: Usually faceted in a step or mixed cut, sinhalite is an excellent choice for jewelry. It is rare, but some gems of more than 100 carats have been found. Because there is not a huge demand, and because it is rare, it is usually cut only for collectors.

Refractive index:	1.667–1.711
Birefringence:	0.038
Dispersion:	0.018
Specific gravity:	3.47–3.49
Hardness:	6.5
Cleavage:	indistinct
Fracture:	conchoidal
Luster:	vitreous
Notable locations:	Sri Lanka, Tanzania, Burma (Myanmar)
Color:	yellow, dark green, greenish brown

Hambergite

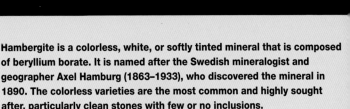

Class: carbonates (borates)

Crystal system: orthorhombic

Composition: beryllium hydroxyborate

Habit: prismatic or bipyramidal

Hambergite is a colorless, white, or softly tinted mineral that is composed of beryllium borate. It is named after the Swedish mineralogist and geographer Axel Hamburg (1863–1933), who discovered the mineral in 1890. The colorless varieties are the most common and highly sought after, particularly clean stones with few or no inclusions.

Properties and characteristics: Hambergite was first discovered in southern Norway, but was not used for gems due to the fact that the material was highly included. Today, Anjanabanoana, Madagascar, is probably the key source of the best gem-quality stones. Some good specimens have also been found in Molo, Burma (Myanmar), but the crystals tend to be small. Hand-sized white crystals have come from Pakistan in the 2000s. Another source is the Himalaya mine, in San Diego County, California. Hambergite forms in flat prismatic orthorhombic crystals that have a vitreous to dull luster. It has the lowest known density of any gem with such a high birefringence. Stones may resemble quartz but hambergite's high birefringence makes it easy to identify.

Cutting, setting, and valuing: Hambergite is a rare and unusual collectors' gem. It is a fragile crystal that is not suitable for jewelry and is normally cut only for collectors. Hambergite is usually faceted in a brilliant or step cut, which gives it the appearance of glass.

Refractive index:	1.553–1.631
Birefringence:	0.072
Dispersion:	0.015
Specific gravity:	2.35
Hardness:	7.5
Cleavage:	perfect in one direction, good in another
Fracture:	conchoidal to uneven
Luster:	vitreous to dull
Notable locations:	Pakistan, Tajikistan, Afghanistan, Madagascar, Burma (Myanmar), India, California in the USA
Color:	colorless, gray-white, yellowish white, white

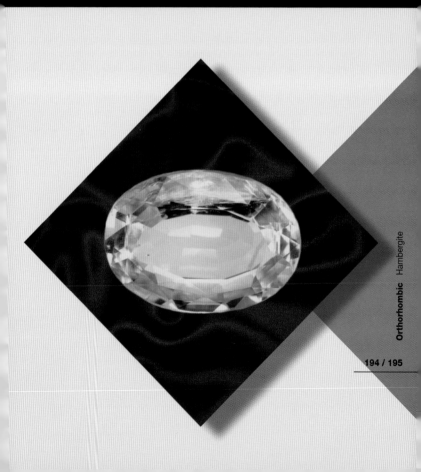

Orthorhombic Hambergite

Prehnite

Class: silicates (sheet silicates)

Crystal system: orthorhombic

Composition: calcium aluminum silicate hydroxide

Habit: globular aggregates; rare tabular to steep pyramidal crystals

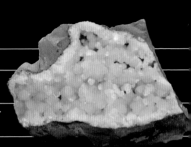

Prehnite was named after the Dutch mineralogist Colonel Hendrik Von Prehn (1733–1785). It was discovered in Jurassic Karoo Dolerite in the Cradock district of the Eastern Cape Province, South Africa, in the late eighteenth century. Prehnite was the first mineral known to be named after a person. It is a bright, almost luminous green mineral, and in many cases has a good luster. Although it is usually a pale yellow-green to grass-green color, prehnite can also be gray, white, or colorless. Massive material often resembles carvable serpentine.

Properties and characteristics: Prehnite is a hydrous, calcium aluminum silicate mineral. Normally found in cavities, and along fractures of basalt and diabase rock, it may also appear in igneous and some metamorphic rocks. Prehnite typically forms thick crusts with a rough and/or crystalline quality. Light green masses have been seen in Scotland. About 90 percent of the world's prehnite reserves are found in Australia, usually in dark green or greenish brown masses. Spectacular crusts and spheroids are found at two localities in Mali, and crystals of many different forms are found in Quebec, Canada. It is also found in South Africa, India, Germany, France, New Zealand, Switzerland, and the USA (New Jersey, Connecticut, Virginia, Pennsylvania, California, Colorado, and Michigan).

Cutting, setting, and valuing: Prehnite is usually cloudy or fibrous, so is translucent. It is considered to be rare and exotic, and it can be faceted (usually in baguette or step cuts) or cut en cabochon (especially when there is a cat's eye effect, or if there are strong, interesting inclusions). It is also carved for ornaments.

Birefringence:	0.030
Dispersion:	weak (less than 0.020)
Specific gravity:	2.80–2.95
Hardness:	6
Cleavage:	distinct in one direction
Fracture:	uneven
Luster:	vitreous to pearly
Notable locations:	Mali, USA, Canada, France, Scotland, Australia, China
Color:	green, yellow-brown, yellow-green

Orthorhombic Prehnite

Zoisite
including Tanzanite

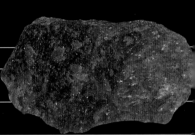

Class: silicates (silicates with paired silica tetrahedra)

Crystal system: orthorhombic

Composition: calcium aluminum silicate hydroxide

Habit: prismatic crystals, often with complex terminations

Zoisite was named for the Slovenian noble, Sigmund Zois (1747–1819), Baron of Edelstein, who financed mineral-collecting expeditions. This mineral was found in 1805 on the Saualpe Mountains, Austria, and was originally called saualpite. In 1967, a blue-to-violet transparent variety was discovered in Tanzania, near Mount Kilimanjaro. This variety was given the name tanzanite. A pink variety called thulite (named after the ancient name for Norway, where it was found) is usually massive. Anyolite is the name frequently applied to gem material that consists largely of massive, apple-green zoisite with bright red corundum.

Properties and characteristics: Zoisite has a complex composition, containing both single silicate tetrahedra and paired tetrahedron groups. It occurs as prismatic, orthorhombic crystals, or in massive form, and is found in metamorphic and pegmatitic rock. Most purple and blue tanzanites are the result of heat treatment: The rough is a yellowish brown color when it is mined, but turns violet-blue when heated. Tanzanite owes its color to vanadium. Some transparent green stones contain both vanadium and chromium. The pink color of thulite is due to the presence of manganese. Green and pink pure massive zoisites have been used as a substitute for jade.

Cutting, setting, and valuing: Transparent material is fashioned into gemstones (usually in a step cut); jewelers prefer to call transparent zoisite of any color tanzanite, as this word is more familiar to the public. Translucent-to-opaque anyolite is usually carved into sculptures and other works of art. Zoisite is also cut en cabochon and in cameos. Tanzanite is brittle and should not be worn as a ring stone on a daily basis.

Refractive index:	1.692–1.702 (gem varieties)
Birefringence:	0.009
Dispersion:	0.018–0.020
Specific gravity:	3.10–3.38
Hardness:	6
Cleavage:	perfect in one direction
Fracture:	even
Luster:	vitreous to pearly
Notable locations:	Tanzania, Pakistan, North Carolina in the USA, Australia
Color:	gray, yellowish brown, greenish, pink (thulite), blue-to-violet (tanzanite)

Staurolite

Class: silicates (silicates with isolated silica tetrahedra)

Crystal system: orthorhombic

Composition: (magnesium or iron) aluminum silicate hydroxide

Habit: prismatic crystals, often twinned

Staurolite is known as "fairy stones" or "fairy crosses," as it naturally occurs in the shape of a cross. The name comes from the Greek words *stauros*, meaning "cross" and *lithos*, meaning "stone," and it has been considered a good luck charm and worn as an amulet for centuries, particularly by Christians.

Properties and characteristics: Staurolite is well known for its twinned crystals. These are classic "penetration-type" twins, which look as if two crystals are growing in and out of each other. There are two twin types—one that is about 60 degrees (the most common) and the other about 90 degrees (which is the most valuable). Staurolite occurs with white micas, almandine garnet, kyanite, and other metamorphic minerals, and it has a distinct pleochroism. Staurolite is reddish brown, brown, and black in color, and it is found in Brazil, Russia, the UK, France, Italy, and the US. Rarely, it is transparent enough to facet as a gemstone; these transparent pieces are brown or green, and pleochroic.

Cutting, setting, and valuing: Most staurolites are mounted as uncut twinned crystals. Copies of staurolite crosses are common, but generally are made out of clay or ceramic material, and show polishing marks. Faceted staurolites are quite rare because it is unusual to find crystals that are both light colored and large enough to be faceted. When they are faceted, however, baguette and step cuts are most common. Stones can be cut en cabochon, or as cameos.

Refractive index:	1.721–1.762
Birefringence:	0.011–0.015
Dispersion:	0.023
Specific gravity:	3.65–3.79
Hardness:	7–7.5
Cleavage:	distinct in one direction
Fracture:	subconchoidal
Luster:	vitreous to dull
Notable locations:	Tennessee, Georgia, Virginia, and Montana in the USA, Russia, Brazil, Scotland, Italy, and France
Color:	reddish brown, brown, and black

Orthorhombic Staurolite

Dumortierite

Class: silicates (silicates with isolated silica tetrahedra)

Crystal system: orthorhombic

Composition: hydrous aluminum borosilicate

Habit: usually fibrous to massive; sometimes columnar crystals

Dumortierite is a borosilicate mineral. It is most commonly used as an ornamental stone, particularly when it is in massive form or included in rock crystal quartz. Dumortierite is most often a hard opaque gemstone, which is generally pale denim blue in color, but can also be pink, violet, green, or brown; very occasionally, it has been found as transparent red-brown gem material. Dumortierite was first identified in 1881 by the French mineralogist M. F. Gonnard, who named it after the French paleontologist Eugene Dumortier (1802–1873).

Properties and characteristics: Dumortierite is usually found in metamorphic rocks that are rich in aluminum, most often in contact metamorphic regions or pegmatites. It can alter to the mineral pyrophyllite. A variety of quartz called dumortierite quartz is massive colorless quartz that is made blue or green by dumortierite crystal inclusions. Dumortierite is sometimes confused with other ornamental stones such as sodalite, lazurite, and lazulite. Dumortierite is pleochroic, appearing to change from red to blue and purples. Some material fluoresces blue under longwave UV light (or white in shortwave UV light). The substitution of iron and manganese for aluminum causes the color variations.

Cutting, setting, and valuing: Although massive material is not used as a faceted gemstone because of its lack of clarity, dumortierite is popular because it is hard and has an intense color. Massive dumortierite can be carved into cabochons, beads, sculptures, eggs, and spheres. Transparent varieties are very rare, but they have been successfully cut as gems.

Refractive index:	1.686–1.723
Birefringence:	0.037
Dispersion:	strong
Specific gravity:	3.26–3.41
Hardness:	8 (massive varieties: 7)
Cleavage:	good in one direction, distinct in one direction
Fracture:	fibrous
Luster:	vitreous
Notable locations:	Madagascar, France, Sri Lanka, Brazil, and Arizona and California in the USA
Color:	blue, violet, brown, pink, bluish green, greenish

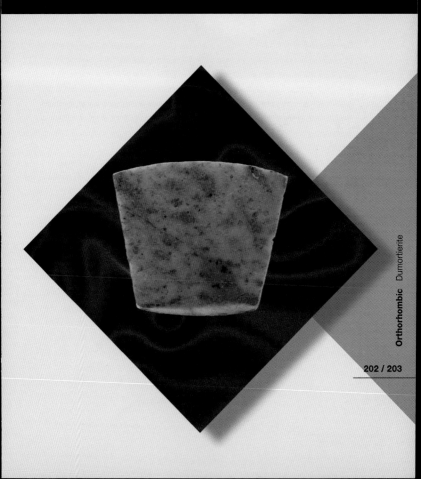

Orthorhombic Dumortierite

Beryllonite

Class: phosphates

Crystal system: monoclinic

Composition: sodium beryllium phosphate

Habit: tabular to short prismatic crystals

Beryllonite is a rare beryllium mineral that has, to date, been found in only a few locations. It was described in 1888 by the American geologist James Dwight Dana (1813–1895), one of the world's foremost mineralogists, and named beryllonite for its beryllium content. Beryllonite was first discovered as highly complex crystals as well as in broken fragments in a granite vein at Stoneham in Maine, USA. It is most commonly associated with feldspar, smoky quartz, beryl, and columbite.

Properties and characteristics: Beryllonite has tabular to prismatic monoclinic (resembling orthorhombic) crystals, which vary from being entirely colorless to pale straw or pastel yellow; the crystals are transparent. Twinning is common and the crystals occur in several forms. Beryllonite forms from pegmatitic dikes and is often confused with more common pegmatite minerals, such as feldspar. This rare gem was previously found only in Maine, but a discovery in Brazil produced beautiful stones. Stones have also been found in Finland and Zimbabwe, as well as Afghanistan. Cat's eyes can occur.

Cutting, setting, and valuing: Beryllonite can be cut as gems, but the mineral lacks the color, fire, and hardness to be a popular gemstone. Some crystals have been cut and faceted (usually in cushion, pear-shape, or brilliant cuts). However, the refractive index is no higher than that of quartz, so they do not make particularly noteworthy gemstones. Most cuts are made for collectors. Cat's eyes are cut en cabochon.

Refractive index:	1.553–1.562
Birefringence:	0.009
Dispersion:	0.010
Specific gravity:	2.80–2.85
Hardness:	5.5
Cleavage:	perfect in one direction, good in one direction
Fracture:	conchoidal
Luster:	vitreous
Notable locations:	Maine in the USA, Minas Gerais in Brazil, Nuristan in Afghanistan
Color:	colorless, white to pale yellow

Monoclinic Beryllonite

Brazilianite

Class: phosphates

Crystal system: monoclinic

Composition: aluminum sodium hydroxyphosphate

Habit: equant or spearhead-shaped crystals

Brazilianite is both rare and unusual—one of the few transparent phosphate minerals that is used as a gemstone. It was first discovered in 1944 near Conselheiro Pena, Minas Gerais, in Brazil. It was originally believed to be chrysoberyl because of its color; however, further study showed that it has a unique habit and a lower hardness. Eventually, brazilianite was found to be a new mineral, and named in honor of the country where it was found.

Properties and characteristics: Brazilianite looks somewhat like forsterite (peridot), but the bright yellow-green color is more interesting. It is found in phosphate-rich pegmatites. The largest crystals measure almost 5 in (12 cm) in length and weigh up to 2 kg (10,000 carats). Smaller crystals have also been found in New Hampshire in the United States. Some of the small crystals found are colorless.

Cutting, setting, and valuing: Brazilianite's value is reliant upon the color and brightness. The colorless, transparent gemstones are less expensive than those with a deep yellow or green hue. It is considered to be more precious than its phosphate mineral cousin, apatite. The crystals are brittle and fragile, chipping easily and breaking along the direction of cleavage, which can make this stone difficult to cut. However, careful lapidaries have faceted brazilianite as cushion, baguette, briolettes, brilliant, and oblong step-cut gems. Most gems are under five carats, but some large stones have been cut, including specimens of 19 and 23 carats.

Refractive index:	1.603–1.623
Birefringence:	0.020
Dispersion:	0.014
Specific gravity:	2.94–3.00
Hardness:	5.5
Cleavage:	good in one direction
Fracture:	conchoidal
Luster:	vitreous
Notable locations:	Conselheiro Pena and other mines in Minas Gerais, Brazil; Smith Mine, Newport, New Hampshire in the USA
Color:	yellow to green

Monoclinic Brazilianite

**Diopside was named in 1800 from the Greek words *di-*, meaning "double"
and *opsis*, meaning "view," which is a reference to its pleochroism.
Varieties of diopside include chrome diopside (a chromium-rich diopside
known for its deep green color, found in diamond pipes), violan (a rare
massive blue variety found in Italy), cat's eye diopside (green with
inclusions of rutile needles), and star diopside (a star with four rays).**

Properties and characteristics: Diopside is a calcium magnesium silicate
found in impure limestone that has metamorphosed, as well as in meteorites
and igneous basalts. Diopside is a part of an important series of the pyroxene
group, which includes the minerals hedenbergite and augite. Gem-quality
diopsides are predominantly mined in Siberia, Italy, Sri Lanka, Brazil,
Madagascar, South Africa, and Pakistan. China is becoming an increasingly
important source for a variety of light green diopside, which is known as
tashmarine. Star and cat's eye diopside is mainly mined in India, while chrome
diopside is normally mined in Yakutia, Siberia.

Cutting, setting, and valuing: Diopside creates some excellent pieces
for collectors, and specimens from some of the most famous localities are
expensive and very valuable. Diopside is faceted into gems for collectors
(normally as brilliant, baguette, and step cuts). Polished specimens that
contain asterisms or cat's eyes are cut en cabochon. Chrome diopside is
mostly available in small sizes; large sizes are very rare. Star diopside is
usually black or blackish green, and cut into round or oval cabochons.

Refractive index:	1.675–1.701 (for gemmy material)
Birefringence:	0.026
Dispersion:	weak to distinct
Specific gravity:	3.23–3.33
Hardness:	5.5–6
Cleavage:	good in 2 directions at 90° angle
Fracture:	conchoidal
Luster:	vitreous
Notable locations:	Burma (Myanmar), Russia, Sri Lanka, India, China, Madagascar, California in the USA; Kenya, Switzerland
Color:	colorless, green, brown, blue, purple, white, and gray

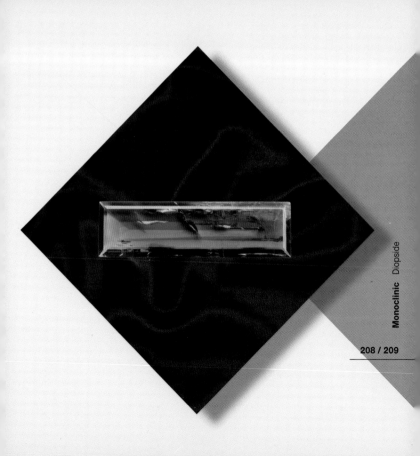

Monoclinic Diopside

Meerschaum
Sepiolite

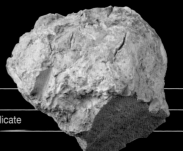

Class: silicates (sheet silicates)

Crystal system: monoclinic

Composition: hydrated magnesium silicate

Habit: massive, claylike nodules

Meerschaum is a soft, white mineral, also known as sepiolite. It is found as compact, dense masses, which have a chalky or earthy appearance. The source of its name is disputed; most think it is named for the German word for "sea froth," but another possible source is the term *mertscavon*, used by Levantine traders. It was named sepiolite by the mineralogist E. F. Glocker—largely because of its resemblance to the bones of the sepia squid (cuttlefish).

Properties and characteristics: Meerschaum is an opaque mineral, normally pale in hue, with whites, grays, or creams being most popular. It breaks with a conchoidal or fine, almost crumbly fracture, and occasionally though rarely, it is fibrous in consistency. Its hardness is very low (about two), and it can be easily scratched with a nail. Most commercial meerschaum is found in Turkey—in particular from the plain of Eskisehir. Its source is alluvial deposits, where it occurs in knobbly, irregular masses, from which it is extracted. Other sources are Greece, France, Czech Republic, Spain, Morocco, and the USA.

Cutting, setting, and valuing: Meerschaum is normally used to fashion pipes, including hookah mouthpieces, cigarette holders, jewelry beads, boxes (which can be both smooth and carved), small carvings (such as eggs and chess pieces), and thimbles. It is soft enough to be easily carved, making it a popular material for this purpose. Carvings are then dried in a kiln and often waxed. Many meerschaum carvings are incredibly intricate, and valued as objets d'art.

Birefringence:	not applicable
Dispersion:	not applicable
Specific gravity:	about 2, but dry material may float on water
Hardness:	2
Cleavage:	perfect
Fracture:	conchoidal
Luster:	dull to earthy
Notable locations:	Turkey, Greece, France, Czech Republic, Spain, Morocco, USA
Color:	ivory-white, cream-yellow, light tan, gray, pinkish, or greenish

Monoclinic Meerschaum

Spodumene

Class: silicates (single chain silicates)

Crystal system: monoclinic

Composition: lithium aluminum silicate

Habit: bladed crystals, often striated along their length

Spodumene is a transparent to translucent gemstone. Transparent, richly colored spodumene comes in two varieties—kunzite and hiddenite. The name spodumene comes from the Greek *spodoumenos*, meaning "burned to ash," which refers to the dry ashy appearance of non-gem crystals. It was named in 1800 by Brazilian naturalist B. J. D'Andrada e Sylva (1765–1838). The term kunzite comes from the name of the New York mineralogist and gemologist G. F. Kunz, who first described it in 1902. Hiddenite is named after the American exploration geologist W. E. Hidden, who first discovered it in North Carolina in 1879.

Properties and characteristics: Spodumene is composed of lithium aluminum silicate. Spodumene is a rock-forming mineral found in various granites and in pegmatites. It was mined for its lithium content in Sweden, Ireland, Madagascar, Brazil, Mexico, Canada, and North Carolina in the USA. Gem spodumene is collected in Brazil, California, Pakistan, and Afghanistan. The mineral is strongly pleochroic and therefore cutters are required to ensure that the stone is in the best position to provide the deepest color. Kunzite is rich in manganese, which provides its beautiful pink-to-lilac color; this color is not light-fast, and fades. Kunzite is more common than chromium-rich green hiddenite, which is mined only in North Carolina. Yellow-green spodumene may be colored by irradiation, and should not be mistaken for hiddenite.

Cutting, setting, and valuing: Spodumene is a fairly soft gemstone; it is suitable for use in pendants but not in jewelry that requires a harder stone (such as rings). It is commonly faceted (usually in brilliants, briolettes, or step cuts). Both kunzite and hiddenite are very popular with collectors.

Refractive index:	1.660–1.675
Birefringence:	0.015
Dispersion:	0.017
Specific gravity:	3.17–3.19
Hardness:	7
Cleavage:	perfect in one direction, good in one direction
Fracture:	splintery
Luster:	vitreous
Notable locations:	Brazil, Afghanistan, Pakistan, USA
Color:	white, colorless, gray, pink, lilac, violet, yellow, and green

Monoclinic Spodumene

Epidote

Class: silicates (silicates with silica tetrahedra in pairs)

Crystal system: monoclinic

Composition: calcium iron aluminum silicate hydroxide

Habit: long prismatic, often striated vertically

The best known color of epidote is "pistachio" green, and this massive mineral is also called pistacite, in reference to its color. The name epidote is from the Greek *epidosis*, meaning "addition" or "increase," which is believed to refer to the fact that some of the crystal faces of this mineral are longer than others. Epidote is famously known from Green Monster Mountain in Alaska, and also from India, Sri Lanka, and Brazil. The chrome green variety of epidote is known as tawmawite, in which up to 11 percent of the aluminum in its formula is replaced by chromium.

Properties and characteristics: Epidote is the chief member of a silicate mineral group, which normally occur in low-grade, calcareous metamorphic rocks and also in igneous rocks, where they have altered from feldspar, pyroxene, and amphibole minerals. As a calcium aluminosilicate, epidote forms pistachio-green fibrous or granular masses, disseminated grains, or dark green elongated crystals, which have perfect cleavage in one direction. With both single and double silicate tetrahedral groups, epidote is a structurally complex mineral. There is a strong pleochroism, showing yellow, green, and brown, depending on direction. Epidote often forms inclusions in quartz.

Cutting, setting, and valuing: Epidote is a very common mineral, but a rare collector's gem. Despite its hardness and deep color, epidote is not commonly cut and polished as a precious gem because the large crystals are rarely clear enough to facet. Cushion and step cut are the most common faceted cuts.

Refractive index:	1.736–1.770 (for gem material)
Birefringence:	0.034
Dispersion:	0.030
Specific gravity:	3.4
Hardness:	6.5
Cleavage:	perfect in one direction
Fracture:	even
Luster:	vitreous
Notable locations:	USA, Sri Lanka, India, Burma (Myanmar), Madagascar, Pakistan, Austria, Norway, Switzerland
Color:	yellow green, dark green, brownish green, rich chrome green, black

Titanite
Sphene

Class:	silicates (silicates with isolated silica groups)
Crystal system:	monoclinic
Composition:	calcium titanium silicate
Habit:	wedge-shaped crystals, sometimes twinned

Titanite is named for its titanium content. It is also known as sphene (after the Greek word for wedge, because its habit is usually wedge-shaped). The gem is usually green or yellowish green, but almost all other colors can occur.

Properties and characteristics: Titanite has a higher dispersion than diamond, making it a brilliant, fiery gem. It also has a strong pleochroism. When stones are transparent, they are renowned for their strong trichroism, and the three colors presented are different according to the body color of the stone. Titanite occurs as an accessory mineral in igneous rocks, schists, gneisses, and other metamorphic rocks. Twinning is common, and crystals from Pakistan are almost always twinned. Titanite is found in a variety of locations worldwide, including Mexico, Brazil, Canada, the USA, Sri Lanka, Madagascar, Switzerland, Italy, Pakistan, and Russia. Trace impurities of iron and aluminum are almost always in attendance. Inclusions can create a chatoyant effect in some stones. The concentrated green color of chrome titanite comes from the presence of chromium.

Cutting, setting, and valuing: Madagascar is the source for much facetable material, and 10-carat cut stones are readily available. As a gemstone, titanite is often a luxurious greenish yellow, and faceters must use a fine lap for cutting. Brilliant, baguette, and mixed cuts are popular with serious collectors. Chatoyant varieties may be cut en cabochon.

Refractive index:	1.885–2.050
Birefringence:	0.105–0.135
Dispersion:	0.051
Specific gravity:	3.52–3.54
Hardness:	5.5
Cleavage:	distinct in one direction, imperfect in two directions
Fracture:	subconchoidal
Luster:	adamantine to resinous
Notable locations:	Sri Lanka, Tamil Nadu in India, Pakistan, Brazil, Madagascar, Mexico
Color:	brown, green, yellow

Monoclinic Titanite

Orthoclase

Class: silicates (framework silicates)

Crystal system: monoclinic

Composition: potassium aluminum silicate

Habit: short prismatic or tabular crystals; also massive

The name orthoclase comes from the Greek words *orthos*, meaning "upright," and *klasis*, meaning "fracture," which alludes to the fact that its two cleavages are at right angles to one another. It belongs to the feldspar family of minerals. These are common around the world, and include the gems moonstone, amazonite, and labradorite (spectrolite). Orthoclase is a potassium-rich feldspar.

Properties and characteristics: The orthoclase composition has three different crystal structures based on the temperature at which it was formed—orthoclase, microcline, and sanidine. Orthoclase is a common constituent of most granites and other igneous rocks, and is often found in masses and large crystals within pegmatites. It is also found in metamorphic rocks, such as schist and gneiss. Twinned crystals are quite common. Transparent, colorless orthoclase occurs mainly in Madagascar, as well as in Sri Lankan and Burmese gem gravels, where cat's eyes and asterisms are present in some specimens. The yellow color in some transparent material is due to iron.

Cutting, setting, and valuing: Its hardness makes orthoclase suitable for jewelry, particularly in pendants, earrings, and pins (but not rings). It is normally faceted in brilliant and mixed cuts; when there is chatoyancy, it is cut en cabochon. Although the mineral can be found across the earth, crystals that are suitable for gems are scarce.

Refractive index:	1.522–1.527
Birefringence:	0.005
Dispersion:	0.012
Specific gravity:	2.56
Hardness:	6
Cleavage:	perfect cleavage in one direction, good cleavage in another
Fracture:	uneven
Luster:	vitreous
Notable locations:	Madagascar, Sri Lanka, Burma (Myanmar)
Color:	colorless, yellow

Monoclinic Orthoclase

Moonstone
Orthoclase

Class: silicates (framework silicates)

Crystal system: monoclinic

Composition: potassium aluminum silicate

Habit: short prismatic or tabular crystals;
also massive

Moonstone is a variety of orthoclase feldspar that shows a flash of white-to blue-white color when viewed at the appropriate angle. The soft glow of this sheen resembles moonlight, so the stone is called moonstone. The sheen itself is called schiller or adularescence, and is due to parallel layers of albite (sodium aluminum silicate) in the feldspar structure. The term adularescence is derived from the name adularia, which refers to colorless, transparent orthoclase (originally from Adular-Bergstock in Switzerland) that displays a bluish white sheen.

Properties and characteristics: Orthoclase is found as a rock-forming mineral in igneous, plutonic, and metamorphic rocks, but rarely as moonstone. Adularia is found in low-temperature hydrothermal deposits. Moonstone comes in a variety of colors and shades, but is most often a whitish blue. Characteristic microscopic inclusions look like small caterpillars in the gem. Polished moonstones from Burma (Myanmar) sometimes exhibit chatoyancy (a narrow band of reflected light that produces a cat's eye effect). A variety with multicolored sheen, known as rainbow moonstone, is a related calcium-rich plagioclase feldspar.

Cutting, setting, and valuing: As a gemstone, moonstone is highly regarded for its beauty. Stones of a large size and fine quality are infrequent; however, moonstone is generally inexpensive. Certain varieties, particularly those that are larger and deeper blue, are highly prized by collectors. The highest quality and most sought-after moonstones come from Sri Lanka. The best moonstone has a blue sheen and almost perfect clarity, and its body color is almost colorless. Moonstones can be faceted in a cushion cut, or, particularly when there is asterism or chatoyancy, cut en cabochon. Cameos are also popular.

Refractive index:	1.520–1.525
Birefringence:	0.005
Dispersion:	0.012
Specific gravity:	2.56–2.59
Hardness:	6
Cleavage:	perfect cleavage in one direction, good cleavage in another
Fracture:	uneven
Luster:	vitreous
Notable locations:	Sri Lanka, Burma (Myanmar), India, Brazil, Madagascar, USA, Tanzania, Switzerland
Color:	colorless to gray, brown, yellow, green, or pink, with white to blue sheen

Monoclinic Moonstone

Euclase

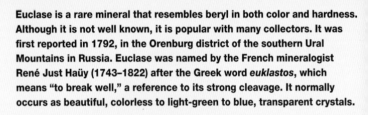

Class: silicates (silicates with isolated silica groups)

Crystal system: monoclinic

Composition: beryllium aluminum silicate hydroxide

Habit: flattened prismatic crystals with complex terminations

Euclase is a rare mineral that resembles beryl in both color and hardness. Although it is not well known, it is popular with many collectors. It was first reported in 1792, in the Orenburg district of the southern Ural Mountains in Russia. Euclase was named by the French mineralogist René Just Haüy (1743–1822) after the Greek word *euklastos*, which means "to break well," a reference to its strong cleavage. It normally occurs as beautiful, colorless to light-green to blue, transparent crystals.

Properties and characteristics: Euclase is most commonly found in granitic pegmatites, alongside other gem minerals such as topaz and various beryls. It is easily identified by its crystal form, which is normally confused only with the accessory mineral barite or sky-blue celestine. Euclase that has been weathered out of its source rock and washed downstream can sometimes be found in placer deposits with gold. Euclase also forms massive fibrous aggregates.

Cutting, setting, and valuing: Well-formed crystals sometimes have sufficient clarity to be cut as gems. The gemstones are normally found in the typical sapphire-blue and blue-green colors, and these are usually the most sought after. Good specimens are coveted by collectors. Euclase's strong cleavage can make it difficult to cut. When faceted, the step cut is most common. Zimbabwean stones command a premium, as do those that are evenly colored. Because of the rarity of this mineral, good stones attract a high price.

Refractive index:	1.652–1.672
Birefringence:	0.020
Dispersion:	0.016
Specific gravity:	3.10
Hardness:	7.5
Cleavage:	perfect in one direction
Fracture:	conchoidal
Luster:	vitreous
Notable locations:	Zimbabwe, Minas Gerais in Brazil, Kenya, Tanzania, Ural Mountains in Russia, Colombia
Color:	colorless, blue-green, blue

Monoclinic Euclase

Jadeite
Jade

Class: silicates (single chain
   silicates)

Crystal system: monoclinic

Composition: sodium aluminum
   silicate

Habit: massive (interlocking crystals
under magnification); blocky crystals rare

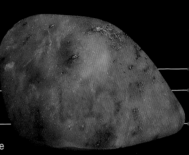

Jadeite is one of the two minerals known as jade, which is the gem
variety of jadeite. The other jade mineral is nephrite, a variety of
tremolite. In fact, the two minerals were thought to be one mineral until
1863, when it was discovered that they have different mineralogical
properties. The name comes from the Spanish *piedra de ijada*, meaning
"stone of the side," referring to the belief that it could cure kidney stones
and other kidney ailments. It has been used for centuries in Central
America as an ornamental stone, and in China and India since the 1700s.

Properties and characteristics: Jadeite is found in sodium-rich serpentinous
rocks, which have been strongly metamorphosed. The color is due to the
presence of trace elements; an emerald green color is the result of chromium;
duller green, yellow, and brown hues come from iron; and lavender colors from
manganese. Variations in color and translucence are often found in a single
specimen. Central American jadeite may contain a diopside component; the
(very similar) ordered intermediate mineral omphacite is not considered jade.

Cutting, setting, and valuing: Jadeite jade is rarer and more valuable than
nephrite jade. Typically, the most highly valued colors of jadeite are the
intensely green, translucent varieties. Emerald-green jade, known as imperial
jade, is the most valuable form. White has long been considered precious by
the Chinese, who are known for their beautifully crafted jade pieces. Jadeite
is cut into cabochons and beads. Some pieces of jewelry are carved out of an
entire mass of jade. Ornamental sculptures and figures are also carved from
this gem. Brownish jadeite may be etched in acid then polymer-impregnated;
this is called B-jade. Dyed jadeite and dyed quartzite imitating jadeite can be
mistaken for natural-color jade, leading to expensive mistakes.

Refractive index:	1.654–1.667; 1.66 (spot)
Birefringence:	0.013 (usually not seen)
Dispersion:	varies with locality from none to very strong; hard to observe
Specific gravity:	3.30–3.36
Hardness:	7
Cleavage:	good, but rarely observed
Fracture:	splintery
Luster:	vitreous to greasy
Notable locations:	Burma (Myanmar), Russia, China, Kazakhstan, Turkey, Guatemala, and California in the USA
Color:	white, green, lilac, red-brown, yellow, gray to black

Monoclinic   Jadeite

Nephrite
Jade

Class: silicates (double-chain silicates)

Crystal system: monoclinic

Composition: hydrous calcium magnesium silicate

Habit: massive (looks felted under magnification)

Nephrite is a variety of actinolite/tremolite that is composed of tough, hard, interwoven fibres. It is one of the two minerals known as jade; the other is jadeite. Nephrite is more abundant than jadeite and is, therefore, less expensive. Nephrite is a hardy mineral and in primitive times it was used to fashion tools such as axes, knives, and clubs. Nephrite's name comes from the Latin *lapis nephriticus*, meaning "kidney stone"; it was often worn in ancient times to remedy problems affecting the kidneys.

Properties and characteristics: Nephrite is composed of calcium, magnesium, silicon, hydrogen, and oxygen, with some iron replacing the magnesium. Boulders are commonly covered with a brown layer—the result of the iron content being oxidized. The color is determined by the levels of iron present in the mineral. Light colors, such as white, cream, yellow, and gray, contain less iron, while the darker grays and greens contain more. Nephrite is an amphibole (a member of an important group of rock-forming minerals), but because of its fibrous structure, its characteristics are more similar to those of chalcedony. It takes a good polish, creating a glassy layer on the surface.

Cutting, setting, and valuing: Only a tiny percentage (less than one percent) of nephrite extracted is of gem quality. The rest is used for carving or building applications (veneers and laminates are popular). Beads and polished stones are also common. The Chinese word for jade is *yu*, meaning a hard carvable material; as a result, many other carving stones in the Orient may be confused with jade, so caution is needed when buying.

Refractive index:	1.600–1.641
Birefringence:	0.027
Dispersion:	weak
Specific gravity:	2.90–3.02
Hardness:	6.5
Cleavage:	perfect in two directions
Fracture:	splintery
Luster:	vitreous to greasy
Notable locations:	Russia, China, New Zealand, Australia, Canada, and Alaska and Wyoming in the USA
Color:	green, yellow-brown, creamy brown, gray, black

Class: carbonates

Crystal system: monoclinic

Composition: hydrated copper carbonate

Habit: fibrous or needlelike crystals forming layered rounded crusts

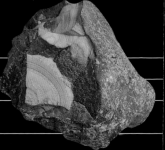

Malachite is an opaque, banded stone, whose colorful bands range from a very light green to almost deep green, and may be curved or angular. This mineral is a copper carbonate, as is blue azurite. Malachite derives its name from Greek word *malache*, meaning "mallow" (a group of related plants with broad green leaves), which is a reference to its color.

Properties and characteristics: Crystals sometimes form as needles that spread out from the host rock in which they are embedded, or as pseudomorphs (false shapes) after other minerals. More often, malachite forms as a mass with evenly spaced, circular bands of pale and deep green. Malachite comes in many forms including thick sheets, large knobs, and green crusts. The massive carvable forms of malachite are its most familiar, while crystalline forms are more unusual. Malachite is usually found with azurite, a blue secondary mineral of copper. Although its energetic green coloring is different, the properties of malachite are very similar to those of azurite, and aggregates of the two minerals are often found together. A mineral sample can have alternating bands of green malachite and blue azurite. Malachite is, however, more common than azurite and is most often found with copper deposits associated with limestone, the source of the carbonate.

Cutting, setting, and valuing: Malachite is often cut en cabochon, to display its characteristic banding. It may also be cut as beads, carved, and used for inlays. It is sometimes cut with an associated mineral such as azure-malachite, and sometimes along with chrysocolla. Tumbled stones of malachite are extremely popular and equally common.

Refractive index:	1.655–1.909
Birefringence:	0.254
Dispersion:	relatively weak
Specific gravity:	about 3.8
Hardness:	4
Cleavage:	perfect in one direction, fair in another direction (for crystals)
Fracture:	uneven
Luster:	vitreous to silky
Notable locations:	Russia, Zaire, Australia, South Africa, Zambia, Arizona in the USA, China, Mexico
Color:	green, bluish green, yellowish green, or blackish green

Monoclinic Malachite

Chrysocolla

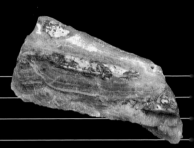

Class: silicates (sheet silicates)

Crystal system: monoclinic

Composition: hydrated copper silicate

Habit: massive; also needlelike crystals

Chrysocolla normally occurs as a bright green or bluish crust. Its name comes from the Greek words *chrysos*, meaning "gold," and *kolla*, meaning "solder" or "glue," which is a reference to the fact that the Greeks used it as a flux for soldering gold. The name was first used by Theophrastus in 315 BCE. "Gem silica" (sometimes identified with chrysocolla) is chalcedony intermixed with chrysocolla.

Properties and characteristics: Chrysocolla is a blue-green hydrated copper silicate mineral, which sometimes contains trace quantities of iron and manganese oxides. It typically forms on the edges of copper ore bodies, and is found as crusts or vein fillings; gem silica is found as glassy botryoidal or rounded masses. Chrysocolla is often found mixed with malachite, turquoise, and azurite; it is, in fact, often confused with turquoise, partly because of its color. A mixture of chrysocolla, malachite, and turquoise from the Gulf of Aqaba region is known as Eilat stone. Chrysocolla in yellow to red-brown jasper makes a rock called "parrot-wing" jasper. Demidovite is a phosphate-bearing chrysocolla occurring in Nizhni-Tagilsk, in the Urals, Russia. Chrysocolla is found wherever copper deposits occur, such as areas of southwestern USA, Chile, Zaire, Australia, France, and England.

Cutting, setting, and valuing: Pure chrysocolla is too soft for use in jewelry, but it can be agatized, which makes it hard enough to polish for cabochons or beads. Parrot-wing jasper is rare, and is sought after by many lapidarists. Translucent, high-quality, gem silica with a uniform color is highly prized.

Refractive index:	1.460–1.570
Birefringence:	0.130
Dispersion:	0.017
Specific gravity:	2.00–2.45
Hardness:	2–4, higher if intergrown with quartz
Cleavage:	absent
Fracture:	conchoidal to splintery
Luster:	vitreous to dull
Notable locations:	New Mexico and Arizona in the USA, Russia, Chile, Peru, Zaire
Color:	sky blue, blue-green, green

Monoclinic Chrysocolla

Azurite

Class: carbonates

Class: carbonates

Crystal system: monoclinic

Composition: copper carbonate
hydroxide

Habit: prismatic crystals with complex
terminations; also layered crusts

**Azurite is a deep blue, copper mineral that is produced when copper ore
deposits have been weathered. Copper gives this stone its remarkable
color. Specimens found at the Chessy-les-Mines, near Lyon in France, are
known as chessylite. The name is derived from the Persian word for blue.**

Properties and characteristics: Azurite is most commonly found as tabular
to prismatic, deep blue crystals with vitreous faces. Crystals are transparent
but very dark, and masses are opaque. In some cases, larger crystals
can appear black, because the color is so intense. Smaller crystals and
crusts yield a lighter, distinctive azure color. Azurite is often associated with
malachite. Stones with large percentages of malachite in azurite are known
as azurmalachite. Azurite is primarily mined in Namibia, Arizona, New Mexico,
Mexico, Australia, China, France, Morocco, Greece, Sardinia, and the Ural
Mountains in Russia.

Cutting, setting, and valuing: Azurite is occasionally used as beads and
cameos, and also as a decorative stone; however, its softness limits its use.
It can be cut en cabochon, and even more rarely faceted. Fine crystal clusters,
knobbly specimens, and interesting combinations with malachite are important
collectors' pieces. Tumbled azurite shows its color to good effect, and crystals
are highly sought after. To improve its appearance and strength, azurite is
occasionally coated with clear wax, and even impregnated with plastic.

Refractive index:	1.730–1.840
Birefringence:	0.110
Dispersion:	relatively weak
Specific gravity:	3.77–3.89
Hardness:	3.5–4
Cleavage:	perfect in one direction, fair in another direction
Fracture:	conchoidal
Luster:	vitreous to waxy
Notable locations:	Arizona in the USA, Namibia, Morocco, France, Australia, Siberia, Russia
Color:	shades of blue, from light to deep

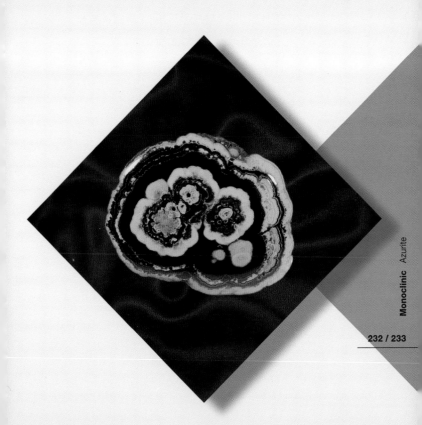

Monoclinic Azurite

Serpentine

Class: silicates (sheet silicates)

Crystal system: monoclinic

Composition: magnesium silicate hydroxide

Habit: usually massive

Serpentine comprises hydrated silicate of magnesium, which is usually green, yellowish green, or bluish green in color with whitish cloudy patches. It sometimes appears in shades of red-to-brown, yellow, or even black. Serpentine gets its name from the word serpent because it resembles the skin of a snake. It is occasionally and improperly called "new jade" or "young jade," due to a Chinese tale that it would turn into nephrite if it were left longer in the ground.

Properties and characteristics: Serpentine is found in many metamorphic and weathered igneous rocks. The name is applied to several associated minerals in a polymorphic group (minerals with similar chemistry but different structures), which includes antigorite, lizardite, orthochrysotile, parachrysotile, and clinochrysotile. The chrysotiles form serpentine asbestos, which should be avoided due to risks of cancer; the massive varieties antigorite and lizardite are fashioned as gems. Yellow-green, deep green, and bluish green translucent serpentine is known as bowenite; this variety is harder than other serpentines. Green serpentine with whitish veins of brucite (from Pennsylvania) is called williamsite, and fine-grained opaque serpentine with banding is known as ricolite. The hardness of serpentine is always directly proportional to its luster.

Cutting, setting, and valuing: Serpentine is suitable for carving and engraving, and it polishes beautifully. It is a prized decorative stone in China. Russian serpentine is a dark, dappled form that is mined in the Ural Mountains, and is highly collectable. Some stones exhibit chatoyancy, and other patterns as the result of fibrous inclusions (possibly asbestos, so be careful), and are cut en cabochon. Serpentine is not expensive. More translucent stones tend to be more valuable. Beware of serpentine being represented as jade.

Refractive index:	1.56 (spot)
Birefringence:	none to 0.002
Dispersion:	weak
Specific gravity:	2.56–2.62
Hardness:	2.5–6
Cleavage:	one good to perfect, not relevant for massive material
Fracture:	fibrous to uneven
Luster:	vitreous to greasy
Notable locations:	India, Pakistan, New Zealand, China, California in the USA, Cornwall in England
Color:	green, yellowish green, blue, yellow, red-brown, brown, black

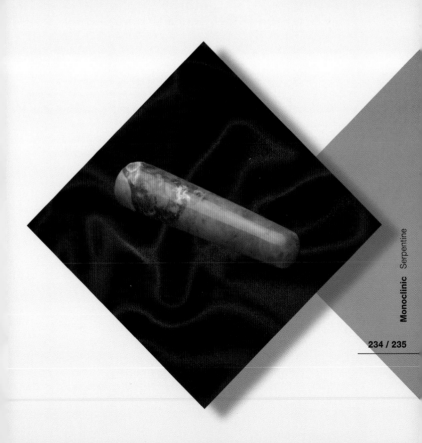

Phosphophyllite

Class: phosphates

Crystal system: monoclinic

Composition: hydrated zinc iron phosphate

Habit: thick tabular and chisel-shaped crystals; "fishtail" twins

Phosphophyllite is an extremely rare mineral, which is composed of hydrated zinc iron phosphate. The name derives from both the phosphate in its chemical composition and the Greek word *phyllon*, meaning "leaf," which is a reference to the mineral's perfect cleavage. It is well known for its enticing, blue-green color and exceptional crystal form.

Properties and characteristics: The best phosphophyllite comes from Bolivia, where it formed in tin-rich hydrothermal veins as a primary precipitate. In fact, gem-quality crystals come only from the Unificada mine, in Potosi City, Bolivia. The first gem crystals were found there in the 1950s, in the Krause vein, and none of those found since have matched their attractiveness and quality. In Germany and in New Hampshire, phosphophyllite is found as an alteration product of primary minerals—in particular, chalcopyrite and triphylite. Crystals from these and other less important locations are small and pallid. Crystals from Bolivia tend to be thick tabular, and can reach 5 in (13 cm) in size. Phosphophyllite fluoresces violet in shortwave UV light. Twinning, particularly "fishtail" twins, are common. Phosphophyllite is transparent.

Cutting, setting, and valuing: Phosphophyllite has long been considered the ultimate in desirable minerals, since it is highly prized by collectors and very uncommon. It is rarely cut (apart from for collectors) because it is both fragile and brittle, and large crystals are simply too precious to be broken down. Bolivian specimens are considered the finest examples of this gem, and outstanding specimens are difficult to come by. When the stone is faceted, brilliant and step cuts are most common. Blue-green is the most sought-after color. Most examples are kept as mineral specimens.

Refractive index:	1.595–1.621
Birefringence:	0.026
Dispersion:	0.012
Specific gravity:	3.1
Hardness:	3.5
Cleavage:	perfect in one direction, distinct in two others
Fracture:	uneven
Luster:	vitreous
Notable locations:	Hagendorf in Germany, Potosi in Bolivia
Color:	blue-green, colorless, light green

Monoclinic Phosphophyllite

Maw-Sit-Sit

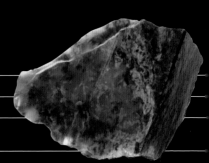

Class: rocks

Crystal system: monoclinic

Composition: chromium-rich rock

Habit: granular rock with grains of kosmochlor, analcime, etc.

Maw-sit-sit is a rare green ornamental rock that has dark green to black veining; it sometimes has white spots. Maw-sit-sit was discovered in Tawmaw, Kachin State, Burma (Myanmar) in the early 1960s, near to the historic imperial jadeite mines in the north of the country. Its name was first used by the natives who mined this rock, and it was first recorded in 1963 by Swiss gemologist Eduard Gübelin (1913–2005).

Properties and characteristics: Like lapis lazuli, maw-sit-sit is a rock, not a mineral, since it consists of many minerals. It is a chromium-rich metamorphic rock, and has a dramatic green base color with black spots, bands, splotches, and whorls. The prevailing mineral is kosmochlor, a sodium-chromium pyroxene. It also contains chromium-enriched jadeite, a chromian amphibole, albite, analcime, and chromite. The high chromium content of this material is responsible for its glowing green color. The only source of maw-sit-sit is the place where it was discovered. It is opaque.

Cutting, setting, and valuing: Because this gem rock is rare, it is typically set into gold rather than silver. It does, however, look beautiful in either metal color, and some collectors have also had stones set into more expensive platinum. The gem is never faceted, but generally cabochon cut or cut into beads. Its rarity means it is normally cut only for collectors.

Refractive index:	1.52–1.74
Birefringence:	none
Dispersion:	not applicable
Specific gravity:	2.46–3.15
Hardness:	6
Cleavage:	not applicable
Fracture:	conchoidal to irregular
Luster:	vitreous to greasy
Notable locations:	Burma (Myanmar)
Color:	mottled bright green with black and white

Monoclinic Maw-Sit-Sit

Lazulite

Lazulite is a rare and fine-looking mineral, which has now become a highly sought-after collectors' item. It was first described in 1795, after deposits were found in Austria. Its name comes from the Persian word *lazhward*, which means "blue." It may be mistaken for lazurite, lapis lazuli, or azurite.

Properties and characteristics: Lazulite is a magnesium aluminum phosphate, formed at relatively low temperatures. The color and strong pleochroism (showing different colors or shades in different directions) is due to iron replacing magnesium in its structure. Transparent crystals are deep blue in color, but crystals are more commonly included and light blue, and there is also granular material. Lazulite forms a solid solution series with the rare phosphate mineral scorzalite; a solid solution series is a set of two or more minerals with elements that freely substitute for one another. The lazulite-scorzalite series ranges from magnesium-rich lazulite to scorzalite, which is rich in iron. Clear lazulite crystals show strong pleochroism from yellowish to colorless and then blue.

Cutting, setting, and valuing: Rapid Creek, in the Yukon Territory, produces some of the highest-quality lazulites. Lazulite is most often used as decorative stones and as rare mineral specimens. It is not particularly abundant, particularly in facetable pieces, although some good stones have been found in India. Fine-quality faceted stones are rare, especially in sizes over a few carats. The mineral can produce glowing, deep blue gems when found in appropriate pieces. It is normally cut en cabochon.

Refractive index:	1.615–1.645
Birefringence:	0.030
Dispersion:	weak
Specific gravity:	3.1–3.17
Hardness:	5.5
Cleavage:	indistinct in two directions
Fracture:	uneven
Luster:	vitreous
Notable locations:	Yukon Territory in Canada, India, Austria, Switzerland, Minas Gerais in Brazil, Georgia and California in the USA
Color:	dark azure blue to bright indigo blue or pale sky blue

Monoclinic Lazulite

Howlite

Class: silicates (chain silicates)

Crystal system: monoclinic

Composition: calcium borosilicate hydroxide

Habit: nodular massive

Howlite is a soft white opaque stone with black or gray inclusions. It was named after Henry How, the Canadian geologist who first discovered it in Windsor, Nova Scotia, in 1868. It is still found there, although in much smaller quantities than it has been in the past. Howlite is known for its wonderful final polish; it is frequently dyed blue as a turquoise imitation.

Properties and characteristics: Howlite is found in evaporite deposits, along with other borate minerals. Howlite is found in Canada (in the eastern provinces of Nova Scotia, Newfoundland, and New Brunswick), and along the western coast of the United States (particularly California). Howlite forms in nodules that look almost like a head of cauliflower. The nodules are often interlaced with veins of black or brown weblike streaks, which adds to their character. Translucent crystals sometimes form on top of the nodules; however, this is fairly uncommon, and usually only found in the material mined in Nova Scotia. Howlite may fluoresce brownish yellow or orange under shortwave UV light.

Cutting, setting, and valuing: Howlite is an inexpensive gemstone. Because it is so soft and permeable, it is easily dyed to look like more expensive gemstones such as turquoise (a dyed stone is pictured, right). The abundance of large sizes, and its softness makes howlite a good stone for decorative objects such as small carvings or jewelry components. Howlite is also sold in its natural state, sometimes under the misleading trade names of "white turquoise" (the aluminum phosphate mineral alunite is also called this), "white buffalo turquoise," or "white buffalo stone." The stone can be carved as beads, or cut en cabochon.

Refractive index:	1.59 (spot)
Birefringence:	0.022
Dispersion:	none
Specific gravity:	2.5–2.6
Hardness:	3.5
Cleavage:	absent
Fracture:	conchoidal
Luster:	dull
Notable locations:	California in the USA, Nova Scotia in Canada
Color:	white with gray to black or brown streaks or markings

Monoclinic Howlite

Gypsum

Class: sulfates

Crystal system: monoclinic

Composition: hydrated calcium sulfate

Habit: many shapes, from tabular to prismatic;
also "roses"

The name gypsum is derived from the Greek word *gypsos*, meaning
"plaster." Selenite is the colorless and transparent variety of gypsum,
and it exhibits a pearly luster. The word selenite comes from the Greek
for "moon," and means, literally, "moonrock," a reference to its moonlike
glow. A variety of gypsum known as satin spar contains hollow tubes,
often giving a chatoyancy effect. Fine-grained massive gypsum is
commonly known as alabaster. Desert roses are rosette-shaped clusters
of gypsum crystals with sand inclusions. Gypsum is used to make plaster.

Properties and characteristics: Gypsum is a very common rock-forming
mineral that forms massive beds. Gypsum also occurs as bladelike crystals
in sediments and clay beds. Crystals that show no point of attachment with
their matrix are called "floaters." The crystals may be curved, and frequently
twin—sometimes forming perfect "fishtail" or "swallowtail" twins. They
may also fluoresce an exquisite pale yellow in shortwave UV light, and may
phosphoresce. Enormous crystals of up to 33 feet (10 meters) in length have
been found in a few locations in Mexico.

Cutting, setting, and valuing: Alabaster is carved for decorative use, such as
artistic sculptures and pottery. Because it is porous, it is easily dyed. The satin
spar variety is sometimes cut en cabochon for collectors because of its strong
cat's eye effect; it is also carved. Fine gypsum specimens are very popular
among mineral collectors, particularly the selenite and desert rose varieties.
Facetable material (selenite) is very rarely cut for collectors, but its softness
makes it inappropriate for jewelry use. Gypsum is not expensive.

Refractive index:	1.52–1.53
Birefringence:	0.010
Dispersion:	strong
Specific gravity:	2.30–2.33
Hardness:	2
Cleavage:	perfect in one direction, distinct in two directions
Fracture:	splintery
Luster:	vitreous to pearly
Notable locations:	Naica in Mexico, Sicily, Utah and Colorado in the USA, Russia
Color:	white to gray, pinkish red, yellow

Monoclinic Gypsum

Datolite

Class: silicates (silicates with isolated silica groups)

Crystal system: monoclinic

Composition: calcium boron silicate hydroxide

Habit: short prismatic or tabular crystals

Datolite was named 1806 by Jens Esmark (1763–1839), a Norwegian professor of mineralogy. The name comes from the Greek word *dateisthai*, meaning "to divide," which refers to the grainy structure of the first examples studied from Arendal, Norway.

Properties and characteristics: Datolite almost always comes in the form of crystals; however, in Michigan copper mines, datolite is found as porcelainlike solid nodules. Datolite is found in well-weathered basalts, and less commonly in other igneous rocks. Datolite is typically found alongside calcite, quartz, fluorapophyllite, prehnite, zeolites, and other minerals in basalt lava rock cavities. Datolite crystals tend to be wedge-shaped with a distinctive, pale green tint. The datolite nodules from Michigan are often more colorful, with purplish hues caused by extremely finely divided copper, and pink and yellow tints that are the result of larger scales and particles of copper that can be seen by the naked eye.

Cutting, setting, and valuing: Although it is not particularly well known, datolite is a popular mineral among mineral collectors. It forms complex crystals, and is most commonly faceted as a step cut. Datolite is not normally used in jewelry; it is cut for collectors only. Gems over 20 carats in weight are rare. Some nodules found in the copper ore areas of Michigan are cut and polished as a decorative stone.

Refractive index:	1.625–1.669
Birefringence:	0.044
Dispersion:	0.016
Specific gravity:	2.90–3.00
Hardness:	about 5
Cleavage:	none
Fracture:	conchoidal to uneven
Luster:	vitreous
Notable locations:	Russia, Michigan and New Jersey in the USA, Norway
Color:	white, colorless, yellowish, reddish, gray, brown, and green

Monoclinic Datolite

Microcline

Class: silicates (framework silicates)

Crystal system: triclinic

Composition: potassium aluminum silicate

Habit: prismatic crystals and massive, often
with exsolved white albite

**Microcline is a common, but not well-known mineral. It has been used as
a semiprecious stone, as the varieties amazonite and perthite. Amazonite
is a deep green variety, while perthite is veined (almost zebra-striped),
the result of lamellar intergrowths found inside the crystal. The name
microcline comes from the Greek words *mikros*, meaning "small," and
klinein, meaning "to incline," because the cleavage planes lean very
slightly away from 90 degrees. Amazonite is named after the Amazon
River, but although amazonite is widely found in Brazil, it is not known
to be found near the Amazon.**

Properties and characteristics: Microcline is a polymorph of orthoclase and
sanidine, minerals that share the same chemistry but have different crystal
structures. Microcline is formed in igneous rocks that cooled slowly. It is
found in granites, granite pegmatites, hydrothermal veins, and schists and
gneisses, and as grains in many sedimentary rocks. Microcline also occurs
in compact crystal aggregates. In some areas, fine amazonite clusters are
mixed with smoky quartz crystals, producing beautiful specimens. Amazonite
gets its green color from small impurities of lead. It is found in the USA, Brazil,
Zimbabwe, Russia, Australia, Namibia, and many other places. The deep
green a strong indicator of microcline. Striated crystals are common.

Cutting, setting, and valuing: Well-shaped crystals and twins, and crystals
of green amazonite, are sought after. Amazonite is usually polished as a
cabochon. Microcline can be faceted in rare cases (for collectors). It is
otherwise cut as beads, cabochons, and cameos, or carved as objects.

Refractive index:	1.522–1.530
Birefringence:	0.008
Dispersion:	0.012
Specific gravity:	2.56–2.58
Hardness:	6–6.5
Cleavage:	perfect in one direction, good in another
Fracture:	uneven
Luster:	vitreous
Notable locations:	India, USA, Canada, Russia, Madagascar, Tanzania, Namibia, Brazil, Zimbabwe, Australia
Color:	blue-green, green, colorless, white, yellow, pink, red, or gray

Triclinic Microcline

Albite

Class: silicates (framework silicates)

Crystal system: triclinic

Composition: sodium aluminum silicate

Habit: tabular to blocky crystals, or massive

Albite is a pure sodium feldspar, and the most sodium-rich member of the feldspar group of minerals, which is more plentiful in the earth's crust than any other group. The name albite comes from the Latin word _albus_, meaning "white," a reference to the mineral's color. It was first reported in 1815 following a discovery in Sweden.

Properties and characteristics: Most of the feldspar gem types are part of the plagioclase group of feldspars. Geologists distinguish between the plagioclase types based on the sodium-versus-calcium content, beginning with albite, which is pure sodium aluminosilicate. As calcium increasingly replaces sodium, the species changes from albite, to oligoclase, to andesine, labradorite, bytownite, and finally anorthite. Albite occurs as blocky crystals in granites and as sheafs of blue-white "clevelandite" crystals in pegmatites; it also occurs in some hydrothermal vein deposits. Albite almost always exhibits twinning—known as lamellar or polysynthetic twinning—in which crystals are made of stacks of microscopically thin layers with contrasting compositions. These twinned layers can appear as grooves, rather like stretchmarks, on the surface of the crystal. Crystals are translucent to opaque, and only sometimes transparent. Like orthoclase, albite forms as moonstone (peristerite).

Cutting, setting, and valuing: Although it is not a hugely popular collectors' stone, albite is used to good advantage as an accessory mineral to other mineral species. The variety clevelandite forms thin white transparent crystals, associated with pegmatite gem crystals such as tourmaline, beryl, and topaz. Although twinned albite crystals are common, crystals showing perfectly formed twins are coveted by collectors. Moonstones are cut en cabochon.

Refractive index:	1.525–1.544
Birefringence:	0.019
Dispersion:	0.014
Specific gravity:	2.60–2.63
Hardness:	7
Cleavage:	perfect in one direction, good in another direction
Fracture:	uneven
Luster:	vitreous to pearly
Notable locations:	Labrador in Canada, Scandinavia, California and Maine in the USA, Colombia
Color:	white or colorless, sometimes shades of blue, yellow, orange, and brown

Triclinic Albite

Oligoclase

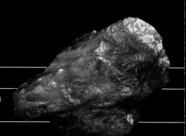

Class: silicates (framework silicates)

Crystal system: triclinic

Composition: sodium calcium aluminum
 silicate

Habit: massive, rare tabular crystals

Oligoclase is not well known, but it is considered to be a gemstone in the
sunstone and moonstone varieties. The name oligoclase was selected by
German mineralogist August Breithaupt (1791–1873) in 1826; it comes
from the Greek words *oligos*, meaning "little," and *klasein*, meaning
"to break," because the mineral was believed to have a less perfect
cleavage than albite.

Properties and characteristics: Oligoclase is part of the plagioclase
feldspar group. It occurs in metamorphic and igneous rocks in, for example,
Norway, USA, India, Russia, and Canada. Moonstone shows a shimmery
glow, which is similar to labradorescence (see page 254), on a transparent or
pale background. Sunstone has flashes of reddish color, which are the result
of hematite or goethite inclusions. It is often known as aventurine feldspar,
because it exhibits aventurescence (a shimmer effect caused by light bouncing
off reflective inclusions within the gem), due to reflections from metallic
inclusions. Oligoclase shows polysynthetic twinning.

Cutting, setting, and valuing: Opaque to translucent varieties are often cut
into cabochons or beads. Their chief feature is the schiller sparkling over the
brown to orangy-red surface. Many stones exhibit a chatoyant effect. Some
oglioclase (such as the completely colorless and transparent glasslike material
found in North Carolina, USA), may occasionally be faceted for collectors.
Iridescent varieties are treasured as collectors' stones.

Refractive index:	1.533–1.552
Birefringence:	0.009
Dispersion:	0.012
Specific gravity:	2.64–2.66
Hardness:	7
Cleavage:	perfect in one direction, good in another
Fracture:	uneven
Luster:	vitreous
Notable locations:	Norway, Sri Lanka, New York in the USA, Russia, Canada, India
Color:	off-white, gray, pale shades of green, yellow, or brown; sunstone has a coppery sheen

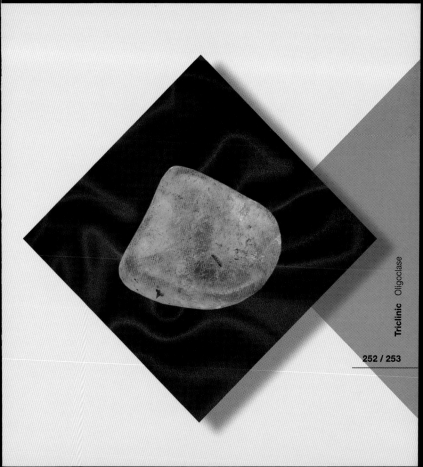

Triclinic Oligoclase

Class: silicates (framework silicates)

Crystal system: triclinic

Composition: sodium calcium aluminum silicate

Habit: thin tabular crystals or massive showing exsolved layers

Labradorite derives its name from the Canadian province, Labrador (near the island of Newfoundland), in which it was first found on St. Paul's Island. Labradorite is normally gray with blue schiller; however, it can occur in a wide variety of colors, including green, orange, red, and yellow.

Properties and characteristics: Labradorite is a translucent to transparent mineral that occurs in crystalline masses; it is also sometimes found in tabular crystals. It is a major constituent of metamorphic and igneous rocks, such as andesite, basalt, diorite, and olivine gabbro. Iridescent material usually comes from Madagascar, while transparent varieties are commonly mined in India. Gemstone varieties from Finland that are highly iridescent are sometimes known as spectrolite. A distinguishing characteristic of labradorite is its schiller effect (light scattered from thin intergrowth layers of different feldspars). This phenomenon is known as labradorescence. Labradorite is normally opaque to slightly translucent, but the flashing effect can create a huge range of colors. Transparent varieties can be found in Canada, Oregon (sunstone, colored by included copper), California, and New Mexico, USA, and other locations.

Cutting, setting, and valuing: The bright orange andesine-labradorite, said to hail from Mongolia, comes as well-cut faceted stones to relatively large sizes. Oregon sunstones are also faceted. Besides these, specimens that display the schiller effect, usually cut en cabochon or as flat pieces, are the most popular cuts for jewelry. Spectrolite from Finland has an exceptionally colorful labradorescence, and is very valuable. Some stones are set as tessarae (glassy tiles) in mosaic jewels. Stones are normally faceted only for collectors.

Refractive index:	1.560–1.572
Birefringence:	0.008
Dispersion:	0.012
Specific gravity:	2.68–2.69
Hardness:	7
Cleavage:	perfect in one direction, good in another
Fracture:	uneven
Luster:	vitreous
Notable locations:	USA, India, Finland, Canada, Australia, Madagascar, Russia, Mexico, possibly Mongolia
Color:	orange, yellow, colorless, gray, green, blue, and red

Triclinic Labradorite

Turquoise

Class: phosphates

Crystal system: triclinic

Composition: hydrated copper aluminum phosphate

Habit: usually massive, rare crystals

Turquoise was one of the first minerals ever mined. For millennia, it has been used in jewelry and in masks in North, Central, and South America and Egypt. It is prized as a gemstone and is possibly the most valuable, non-transparent mineral in the jewelry trade. The name comes from the French word for "Turkish," as it originally reached Europe from Iran via Turkey. Today, most turquoise comes from China, although excellent specimens come from the United States (Arizona and adjoining states), Tibet, Iran, and other places.

Properties and characteristics: Turquoise is a secondary mineral occurring in veins in aluminous igneous rocks, or sedimentary rocks that have been considerably altered, most often in very hot, dry areas. This gemstone is often confused with azurite, variscite, and wardite. Outstanding white or brown matrix stones can be found in southwest America. The intense color is often mottled or veined with brown limonite or black manganese oxide (known as "spiderweb" turquoise). Turquoise stone is a hydrous basic phosphate of copper and aluminum; its colors range from blue to nearly green to white. The replacement of copper by iron and zinc produces a green stone.

Cutting, setting, and valuing: Turquoise should not be overpolished, which can make the color greener and less attractive. Many samples are porous, and the stone is sensitive to sunlight, soap, water, perspiration, and grease. Low-quality turquoises are often dyed or have their colors stabilized. Flat pieces are often used as inlays, or cut as cabochons. It is also cut as beads and cameos, and irregular pieces are set in mosaics. The most expensive and rare turquoises come from Iran and from Lander, Bisbee, Carico Lake, Cerrillos, and other southwestern USA sources. Imitations are common.

Refractive index:	1.61–1.65 (spot)
Birefringence:	not applicable
Dispersion:	not applicable
Specific gravity:	2.60–2.90
Hardness:	5.5–6
Cleavage:	perfect in two directions; unusually unseen
Fracture:	conchoidal and smooth
Luster:	dull to waxy; vitreous in macro-crystals
Notable locations:	Arizona and New Mexico in the USA, Iran, Tibet, China
Color:	turquoise, varying from a light greenish blue to rich blue shades

Triclinic Turquoise

Class: silicates (single chain silicates)

Crystal system: triclinic

Composition: manganese silicate

Habit: massive, or rough tabular crystals

Rhodonite is a manganese silicate, and the manganese causes its rosy colors. Its name comes from the Greek word *rhodon*, meaning "rose," a reference to its distinct color. Massive gem rhodonite was recorded as coming from Massachusetts, USA, as early as 1825.

Properties and characteristics: A manganese silicate, rhodonite also frequently contains the elements iron and calcium. It usually occurs as cleavable to compact masses with a rose-red color, which can lean towards brown because of surface oxidation. Rhodonite is usually associated with black manganese minerals, which are the cause of its characteristic black mottling; this is sometimes called "spiderweb" rhodonite. Facet-quality crystals are found with spessartite in lead ore from Broken Hill, New South Wales, Australia. There are several similar manganese silicates —pyroxmangite, fowlerite, nambulite; some of these may be faceted as well.

Cutting, setting, and valuing: Most faceted stones are under five carats. Any eye-clean (clear to the eye) rhodonite stone over 10 carats is considered to be large. Crystals of rhodonite are not as common as massive rhodonite, but are still considered to be classics by serious collectors. The massive material is cut as beads or cabochons, or carved into objects.

Refractive index:	1.733–1.747
Birefringence:	0.014
Dispersion:	0.010–0.020
Specific gravity:	3.40–3.71
Hardness:	6
Cleavage:	perfect in two directions
Fracture:	uneven
Luster:	vitreous
Notable locations:	Australia, Ural Mountains in Russia, Brazil, Sweden, South Africa, USA
Color:	shades of pink through red

Triclinic Rhodonite

Amblygonite

Class: phosphate

Crystal system: triclinic

Composition: lithium aluminum hydroxyphosphate or fluorphosphate

Habit: crude equant crystals; usually massive

Amblygonite is an excellent collector's stone, particularly in larger sizes and deeper colors. It was first discovered in 1817, in Saxony, Germany, and was described by August Breithaupt. He gave this gem the name amblygonite, from the Greek words *amblys* (meaning "blunt") and *goni* (meaning "angle"), which refers to the mineral's four directions of cleavage. It has been discovered in considerable quantities in California, Spain, Burma (Myanmar), and Brazil. Amblygonite is in the amblygonite mineral group, along with the related minerals griphite, montebrasite, natromontebrasite, tancoite, and tavorite.

Properties and characteristics: This gem is easily confused with similar rockforming minerals, such as quartz and albite; however, its high lithium content and unusual cleavage set it apart. The structure is compact, and it has a higher specific gravity than both quartz and albite. Amblygonite occurs in a wide range of colors, including milky white, taupe, peachy pink, and light or greenish yellow, through to blue, gray, darker pinks and greens, and even brown. Amblygonite is transparent to translucent, and is composed of about 10 percent lithium, which makes it an economical source of this element. Amblygonite is also popular as an ingredient in porcelain enamels, and increases opacity in glass dinnerware.

Cutting, setting, and valuing: The best examples of amblygonite's yellow variety are cut as gemstones, and some samples are clean enough to be faceted. Brilliant or mixed cut are most common. Gems range from 1 to 15 carats. However, this stone is too soft to be popular for jewelry.

Refractive index:	1.611–1.637
Birefringence:	0.026
Dispersion:	0.018–0.019
Specific gravity:	3.01–3.03
Hardness:	6
Cleavage:	in four directions all with varying quality; one direction perfect, two good, one distinct
Fracture:	irregular/uneven, subconchoidal
Luster:	vitreous to pearly
Notable locations:	Brazil, USA, Australia, Burma (Myanmar), Germany, Spain, Canada, and Namibia also produce gem-quality amblygonite
Color:	white or creamy, but can also be colorless or pale yellow, green, blue, beige, gray, or pink

Triclinic Amblygonite

Axinite Mineral Group

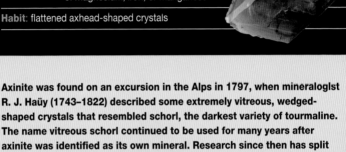

Class: silicates (ring silicates)

Crystal system: triclinic

Composition: calcium aluminum borosilicate hydroxide of magnesium, iron, or manganese

Habit: flattened axhead-shaped crystals

Axinite was found on an excursion in the Alps in 1797, when mineraloglst R. J. Haüy (1743–1822) described some extremely vitreous, wedged-shaped crystals that resembled schorl, the darkest variety of tourmaline. The name vitreous schorl continued to be used for many years after axinite was identified as its own mineral. Research since then has split the axinite group into four species, all of which may be cut as gems: axinite-(Mg), axinite-(Mn), axinite-(Fe), and tinzenite. The name axinite comes from the characteristic ax shape of its crystals.

Properties and characteristics: Axinite forms in metamorphic rocks, which come from calcium-rich sedimentary rocks such as limestone. It is highly trichroic but the flat wedge-shaped crystals are often too slim to make use of the prettier reddish brown and indigo colors visible in some directions. Axinite is often mistaken for chrysoberyl, hessonite, topaz, or tourmaline in the yellow varieties; however, the other colors are more typical. A unique Tanzanian axinite is blue. Axinite is a series name for a group of isostructural minerals that share the same structure but have a different chemistry. They are named according to how much iron, magnesium, manganese, and calcium they contain. For example, iron-rich, lilac-brown to black axinite is called axinite-(Fe), while magnesium-rich, pale blue to gray stones are known as axinite-(Mg). Axinite-(Mn) is yellowish orange and rich in manganese, and tinzenite (the only exception to the way these minerals are named) is yellow and has varying amounts of calcium, iron, and manganese.

Cutting, setting, and valuing: An unusual gemstone, axinite is cut more for collectors than consumers. Faceted stones (normally brilliant or mixed cuts) are generally small. Crystals that are large enough to be made into gems over 10 carats in size are rare.

Refractive index:	1.660–1.68
Birefringence:	0.010–0.012
Dispersion:	0.018–0.020
Specific gravity:	3.18–3.29
Hardness:	7
Cleavage:	good in one direction, poor in two others
Fracture:	conchoidal
Luster:	vitreous
Notable locations:	California in the USA, Russia, Mexico, Brazil, Tanzania, Sri Lanka, Switzerland, Japan, England, France
Color:	lilac brown, but also yellow, yellow-orange, gray, pale blue, and black

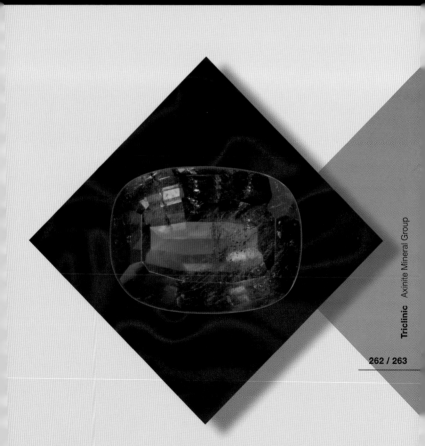

Triclinic Axinite Mineral Group

Kyanite

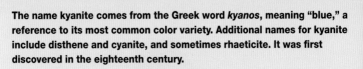

Class: silicates (silicates with isolated silica groups)

Crystal system: triclinic

Composition: hydrous aluminum silicate

Habit: bladed or tabular crystals, sometimes twisted

The name kyanite comes from the Greek word *kyanos*, meaning "blue," a reference to its most common color variety. Additional names for kyanite include disthene and cyanite, and sometimes rhaeticite. It was first discovered in the eighteenth century.

Properties and characteristics: Kyanite is commonly found in schists and gneisses associated with staurolite, garnet, and rutile, as well as in aluminum-rich metamorphic pegmatites. Its distinguishing feature is the fact that its hardness varies depending on the direction of the crystal; in other words, there are different levels of hardness within the same crystal. This phenomenon is known as hardness anisotropy. This aluminum silicate mineral is a polymorph with andalusite and sillimanite, meaning that they share the same chemistry but have different crystal structures. The color is caused by the presence of iron and titanium in blue varieties, and vanadium in those that are green. Kyanite's color is not always uniform. It has a strong pleochroism, appearing violet, blue, or colorless in different directions. There are chatoyant varieties.

Cutting, setting, and valuing: Kyanite has also been used as a gemstone, although this use is limited by its erratic hardness and perfect cleavage. It is normally faceted for collectors, often in the baguette or step cut. Stones showing a chatoyancy are cut en cabochon. The most highly prized kyanites have vibrant blue or blue-green hues.

Refractive index:	1.715–1.732
Birefringence:	0.017
Dispersion:	0.020
Specific gravity:	3.65–3.69
Hardness:	5–7 (directional)
Cleavage:	perfect in one direction, imperfect in another
Fracture:	conchoidal
Luster:	vitreous to pearly
Notable locations:	India, Brazil, Kenya, Burma (Myanmar), Pakistan, Nepal, Norway, USA
Color:	blue, green, colorless

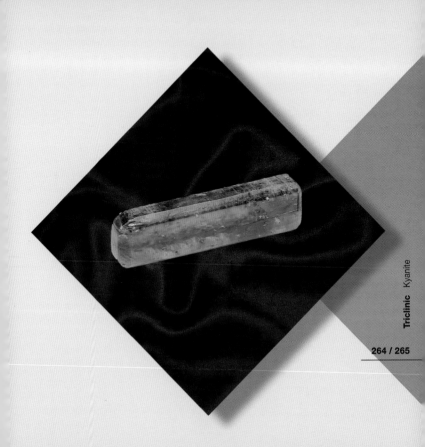

Triclinic Kyanite

Class: mineraloids	
Crystal system: amorphous	
Composition: hydrated silica gel	
Habit: massive, in seams, sometimes as pseudomorphs	

Opal is a mineraloid (so-called because its structure is not genuinely crystalline), which is primarily sourced from Australia. The word opal comes from the Sanskrit word *upala*, meaning "precious stone."

Properties and characteristics: This mineraloid is deposited at relatively low temperatures, and may occur in fissures of most types of rock, especially sandstone, rhyolite, and basalt. The most important opal is precious opal, which shows a play of color when moved. Precious opal may be subdivided into white and black based on the body color of the gem. It is composed of silica spheres organized in close-packed arrangement; the size of the spheres is comparable to the wavelength of light. The color play is the result of the diffraction of light from the different spheres in the opal structure. Opalescence, the milky effects in white opals, is due to scattering of white light by particles within the stone. Opal cat's eye is caused by the presence of parallel fibers or hollow tubes. Crystalline inclusions (such as needles of hornblende, quartz, and goethite) are common. "Cherry" opal comes from Mexico and has a bright orange body color. Some opals from Ethiopia have brown body colors. Pink opal and blue opal from Peru are translucent and colored by included minerals.

Cutting, setting, and valuing: Opals with strong color play are most sought after for gems. Opals that have hues of reds against black are the rarest and most expensive, whereas white and greens are the most common. Cherry, pink, and blue opals are less valuable than those with a play of color. Stones may be faceted (usually in a step cut) or cut en cabochon (particularly when there is chatoyancy or other interesting inclusions). Beads and cameos are also popular, as are doublets (in which the opal is backed by another material). Opals may crack if they dry out. Synthetics and imitations are common.

Refractive index:	1.44–1.46
Birefringence:	none
Dispersion:	none
Specific gravity:	1.98–2.20
Hardness:	5.5–6.5
Cleavage:	none
Fracture:	conchoidal
Luster:	vitreous to dull
Notable locations:	Australia, Mexico, Brazil, Oregon in the USA, Ethiopia, Peru, Hungary
Color:	clear through white, gray, red, orange, yellow, green, blue, pink, brown, and black

Amorphous Opal

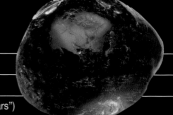

**Obsidian is a natural glass. The term obsidian is believed to have resulted
from a printer's error involving the Latin word *obsianus*, which was meant
to allude to Obsius. He was credited, by the Roman scholar Pliny the
Elder, as discovering this rock in Ethiopia.**

Properties and characteristics: Obsidian is a mineraloid rather than a true
mineral, because it is not crystalline. Instead, it is a cooled volcanic glass rich
in silica and aluminum oxide. Formed from volcanic lava that cooled quickly,
precluding significant crystallization, obsidian may be included with tiny gas
bubbles and other minerals, giving it a variable appearance. The color may be
uniform, or striped, or spotted. Some inclusions give obsidian a metallic sheen,
an iridescence seen as flashes of color or, most commonly, silver or golden
tones. When the sheen is multicolored, the stone is known as "rainbow"
obsidian. Cristobalite crystals produce a snowflake effect (in which case, the
stone is called "snowflake" obsidian). Dark nodules that have been found in
Arizona and New Mexico are known as "Apache tears." Obsidian's typical dark
green, brown, or black color is the result of iron and magnesium. Very rarely,
obsidian can be nearly colorless.

Cutting, setting, and valuing: Obsidian is frequently carved for jewelry—
especially earrings, bracelets and pendants—and into diverse decorative
objects, such as animals. It has some interesting properties as a gemstone:
When cut in one direction, it is jet black; when cut in another, it is an almost
tinny gray. It is normally cut en cabochon, or polished as a stone. It is widely
available, and modestly priced. Red, blue, and green "obsidians" are almost
always artificial glass.

Refractive index:	1.48–1.51
Birefringence:	none
Dispersion:	0.035
Specific gravity:	2.33–2.42
Hardness:	5
Cleavage:	none
Fracture:	conchoidal
Luster:	vitreous
Notable locations:	Italy, Mexico, Scotland, and Arizona, Colorado, Texas, Utah, and Idaho in the USA
Color:	gray to dark green to dark brown and black

Amorphous Obsidian

Moldavite

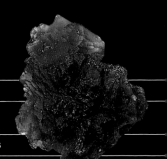

Class: mineraloids

Crystal system: amorphous

Composition: silica glass with aluminum, magnesium, iron, etc.

Habit: aerodynamic nodules or etched shapes

Moldavite is a naturally occurring glass, originally found along the Moldau River in Czechoslovakia in 1787. It is usually dark olive-green in color. The name moldavite comes from the region in which it was first found.

Properties and characteristics: Moldavite is an impact glass, melted from terrestrial rocks by a meteorite impact, thrown into the air, and then cooled as they tumbled through the atmosphere. Moldavite has a diagnostic pattern of striae (internal flowing bands) and long, dumbbell-shaped bubbles that do not appear in manmade glass. Unlike volcanic glass or obsidian, it does not contain any crystals. Outer surfaces range from fairly smooth to rough, and are commonly grooved, as if they have undergone a natural process of etching. Moldavites are one type of tektite. Other tektites include australites from Australia and Tasmania, and billitonites from Malaysia; both of these are commonly black.

Cutting, setting, and valuing: The most highly prized moldavites are deeply grooved, clear green pieces. Moldavites are sometimes cut as gemstones (usually faceted in brilliant or cushion cuts) or put into jewelry as natural uncut pieces to show off their interesting and intricate shapes. Some specimens have been marketed uncut (although they are usually mounted) as cabochons and, more rarely, as little carvings. Fashioned moldavites have been sold under misleading names, such as Bohemian chrysolite, false chrysolite, pseudochrysolite, or water chrysolite. Good-quality moldavite is rare.

Refractive index:	1.48–1.52
Birefringence:	none
Dispersion:	0.022
Specific gravity:	2.30–2.50
Hardness:	5.5
Cleavage:	absent
Fracture:	conchoidal
Luster:	vitreous
Notable locations:	Czech Republic, Austria, Germany
Color:	green to nearly colorless

Amorphous Moldavite

Class: organic

Crystal system: amorphous

Composition: natural resins made of polymerized tree sap (carbon, hydrogen, oxygen, etc.)

Habit: massive rounded nodules, rarely as seams

Amber derives its name from the Arabic word for *ambergris*, a waxy material (which is regurgitated by sperm whales) that is used for making perfumes. The Greeks called amber *elektro*, from which the word electricity is derived; if you rub amber with a cloth it will become charged, creating static electricity. The Latin word *succinum* has also come into usage with mineralogists, as the word succinite, the name of a specific chemical composition of (Baltic) amber.

Properties and characteristics: Amber is a combination of hydrocarbons, resins, succinic acid, and various oils. It is the hardened or fossilized resin of, for instance, the pine tree *Pinus succinifera*, from about 30 million years ago. Amber should not be confused with copal resin which has a similar source but has not polymerized as much, and is therefore not as hardened. Amber is either collected from sea shores, fished from water, or mined in open pits. The most prominent source may be the Baltic Sea, where it washes up on shore from submerged beds. Other locations include Burma (Myanmar), Romania, Russia, the Dominican Republic, Wyoming in the USA, and Venezuela. Amber fluoresces bluish white in shortwave UV light, and yellow in longwave UV light. The color depends on both the source and the number and type of impurities.

Cutting, setting, and valuing: Amber is mostly cut as cabochons, and is known for its inclusions of pollen, insects, leaves, and other organic debris that was originally trapped in the sticky fluid. Amber with identifiable insects and plants are quite valuable. Occasionally, amber is faceted. Fluorescent olive green and blue ambers are also more expensive, but the blue color is said to occur on broken surfaces and fade over time. Most "red amber" is a plastic imitation, and golden amber is also readily imitated in plastic.

Refractive index:	1.54
Birefringence:	none
Dispersion:	none
Specific gravity:	1.08
Hardness:	2–2.5
Cleavage:	none
Fracture:	conchoidal
Luster:	resinous to greasy
Notable locations:	coasts off the Baltic Sea, Sicily, Romania, Dominican Republic, Mexico, Burma (Myanmar)
Color:	yellow, brown, red, orange, colorless; may luminesce blue

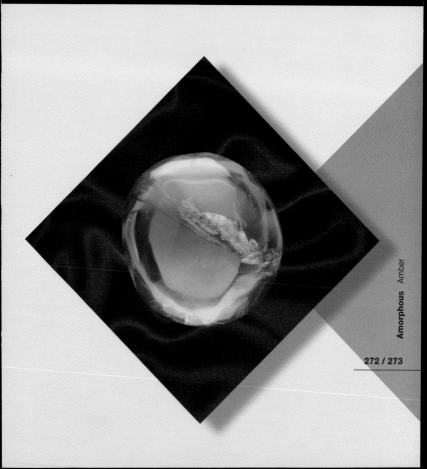

Amorphous Amber

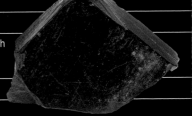

Class: organic

Crystal system: amorphous

Composition: carbon and hydrogen with minor amounts of other elements

Habit: usually massive

Jet (which is known in Russia as gagate) is a black organic substance that is a partially fossilized wood, similar to brown coal. It is a hard, lightweight, glossy black stone that was used in mourning jewelry during the Victorian era. The name jet derives from the French word for the same material: *Jaiet*.

Properties and characteristics: Jet is formed when driftwood is compacted over millions of years. It is usually black, but can be dark brown, and may also contain inclusions of pyrite, which produce a rather brassy color and a distinctive metallic luster. Jet is not considered to be a true mineral, but rather a mineraloid, because its structure is not crystalline. Jet is found in two forms: hard and soft. Hard jet is the result of greater compression than soft jet, and salt and fresh water may also alter the composition. Most jet is from Whitby, in Yorkshire, England, where it has been mined since prehistoric times. It is also found in Spain, France, Germany, USA, and Russia, but these other sources are believed to be inferior to the harder, more flexible Whitby jet. Jet has also been known as black amber, because it may provoke an electric charge when rubbed (rather like amber does). Rubbing also produces a strong odor.

Cutting, setting, and valuing: Jet is frequently cut en cabochon, and polishes well. Beads, cameos and tumbled, polished stones are popular with collectors, and jet is often faceted. The Victorians made elaborate carvings in this material. Although less popular than in the past, genuine jet jewels are still prized by collectors.

Refractive index:	1.66 (spot)
Birefringence:	none
Dispersion:	none
Specific gravity:	1.30–1.35
Hardness:	2.5–4
Cleavage:	none
Fracture:	conchoidal
Luster:	velvety to waxy to dull
Notable locations:	England, Spain, France, USA, Germany, Russia
Color:	black, brownish

Amorphous   Jet

Class:	organic
Crystal system:	various
Composition:	calcium hydroxyl phosphate with organic matter
Habit:	radial structure with "engine turning"

The term ivory was originally used to describe the fabric of an elephant's tusk. Today, with the appropriate name modifier, it also designates the teeth of hippopotamus, narwhal, walrus, and sperm whale. Most of these mammals are endangered species protected by law in the international community. An alternative to ivory is fossil ivory, which is obtained from the remains of mammoths that lived in the northern hemisphere at least 10,000 years ago.

Properties and characteristics: Ivory artefacts are relatively hardwearing because of their density and comparatively high ratio of mineral to protein components. Ivory is smooth, translucent to opaque, and white to light yellow with a greasy to dull polished luster. Occasionally, specimens of bone or ivory are dyed blue with copper salts to imitate a rare, naturally colored fossil ivory known as odontolite. Mammoth ivory with the iron phosphate vivianite on it is naturally blue in places. Some very old ivory carvings and curios may have been carved from the tusks of Asian elephants, who had smaller tusks. Ivory may fluoresce blue to blue-white in UV light. Both elephant and mammoth ivory show "engine turning" patterns along the tooth grain, whereas the teeth of other animals do not show this.

Cutting, setting, and valuing: Before plastics were invented in the late nineteenth century, ivory was widely used for jewelry, buttons, hair combs, and other everyday objects. Its rarity means that it has become increasingly valuable. There are some beautiful contemporary jewelry pieces on the market made of natural vegetable ivory, which is derived from tagua nuts from South America and doum palm nuts from Africa; these ivories are increasing in value. Ivory is normally cut as beads or cameos, or sold as polished stones, inlay, or carvings.

Refractive index:	1.54
Birefringence:	not applicable
Dispersion:	not applicable
Specific gravity:	1.70–1.95
Hardness:	2.5
Cleavage:	none
Fracture:	fibrous
Luster:	dull to greasy
Notable locations:	African elephants, Asian elephants, other animals
Color:	creamy, white, yellow, brown

Various Ivory

Shell
and Tortoise Shell

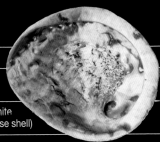

Class: organic

Crystal system: various

Composition: calcium carbonate (most);
organic (tortoise shell)

Habit: oriented layers of calcite and/or aragonite
(most); oriented layers of keratin (tortoise shell)

Shells have long been used for jewelry purposes, and carved into buttons, inlay, cutlery handles, snuff boxes, combs, and much more. Many different types of shells are used for these decorative purposes, including large pearl oysters, abalones, and topshells (which are all valued for their iridescent, mother-of-pearl shell linings), as well as tortoiseshell and conch shells, which are carved into intricate cameos.

Properties and characteristics: Mother of pearl is the inner iridescent layer of a mollusk or snail shell. Mother of pearl is most frequently white, like the color of most pearls. However, that of black Tahitian pearls are dark. Another well-known mother-of-pearl specimen is the Paua abalone from New Zealand, which has a blue-green iridescent color play; the transparent crystals of calcium carbonate which comprise the inner lining of the abalone shell create iridescent colors when light shines on them. Tortoise shell is composed of a complex protein (keratin), which is obtained from the sheath or shield of the hawksbill turtle found in the Malay Archipelago, Indonesia, and Brazil.

Cutting, setting, and valuing: Shells may be polished, carved as cameos, or cut en cabochon to show off their unique patterning. The value of most shells depends on their rarity rather than their beauty. Common shells may be inexpensive, while complete examples of rare species may cost thousands of dollars. Tortoise shell is scarce because sea turtles are now endangered, so it can only be acquired in antique pieces; plastic imitations are usually used instead. Like opals, tortoise shell will crack with age.

Refractive index:	1.55–1.69 (most), 1.55 (tortoise shell)
Birefringence:	not applicable
Dispersion:	not applicable
Specific gravity:	2.6 (carbonate); 1.30 (tortoise shell)
Hardness:	2.5–3
Cleavage:	none
Fracture:	uneven
Luster:	oily to vitreous
Notable locations:	various
Color:	white, gray, yellow, brown, olive, pink, purple (most); mottled golden brown (tortoise shell)

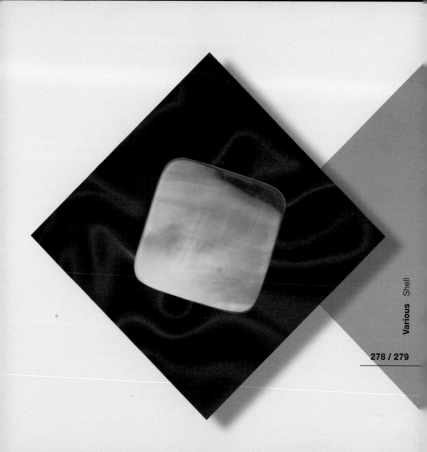

Various Shell

Coral

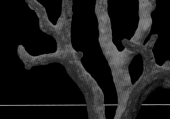

Class: organic

Crystal system: various

Composition: calcium carbonate or organic material

Habit: branches with radial structure

Corals are the product of tiny living creatures, which formed vast settlements in deep warm seas, well before humanity existed. The name coral may come from the Greek *korallion*, meaning the hard calcareous skeleton of the animals from which coral is composed.

Properties and characteristics: Coral polyps (small marine invertebrates) secrete a strong calcium carbonate structure used in jewelry making. Colors usually range from red, orange, and pale pink (angelskin coral) through to a pure, saturated white. Calcareous coral (usually white, pink, red, and orange) exhibits a distinct pattern of parallel stripes, each with a vaguely different color and transparency. Conchiolin coral (made of conchiolin, an organic protein, and normally black, blue, golden, and brown) displays a concentric structure around the axis of the original branch. In most cases, golden coral displays a characteristic fine pimpled appearance as well as a concentric structure and (less commonly) a weak sheen. Coral grows in the warmest seas, and is predominantly found off the coasts of Hawaii, from the Bay of Biscay through into the Mediterranean Sea, the Red Sea, and the Japanese and Australian coasts. Black coral is found off the Cameroon and Hawaiian coasts.

Cutting, setting, and valuing: For the purposes of jewelry, coral is either carved into beads, cameos, or other forms, or is left in its natural branchlike form and polished. It is commonly cut en cabochon, to exhibit its attractive vitreous luster. The most valued colors are those that are deep red in color (called noble coral) and pinks are also popular and expensive. Golden coral is also precious due to its rarity, and some black coral is treated with peroxide to turn it golden in color. The conchiolin corals are vulnerable species and there are limits on their collection and export.

Refractive index:	1.49–1.65 (calcareous), 1.56 (conchiolin)
Birefringence:	0.20 (calcareous)
Dispersion:	not applicable
Specific gravity:	2.6–2.7 (calcareous); 1.34 (conchiolin)
Hardness:	3.5 (calcareous)
Cleavage:	none
Fracture:	uneven (calcareous)
Luster:	waxy to vitreous
Notable locations:	warm sea beds near Hawaii, the Bay of Biscay, the Mediterranean and Red Seas; Japanese, African, and Australian coasts
Color:	white, pink, red, orange, blue to violet, golden, brown, and black

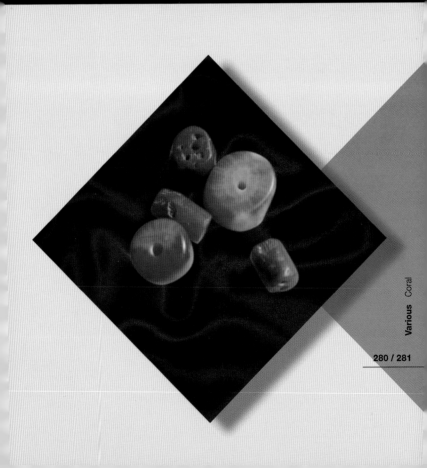

Various Coral

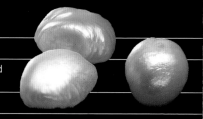

Class: organic

Crystal system: not applicable

Composition: calcium carbonate and conchiolin

Habit: round to baroque shapes

Pearls were first successfully cultured in Japan in the early twentieth century, and initially licensed in 1907. Before that time only natural pearls were available, and the prices were very high and supplies sporadic at the very best. Today, cultured pearls are available in virtually any size, shape, and color.

Properties and characteristics: Pearls are organic gems, created when an oyster or another mollusk covers a foreign object with beautiful layers of nacre (composed of layers of calcium carbonate and an organic protein called conchiolin). In natural pearls, this process occurs naturally, and the pearls are almost 100 percent nacre. In bead cultured pearls, shell beads (nuclei) are placed inside an oyster and the oyster is returned to the water. Tissue-nucleated cultured pearls do not have shell bead cores. When the pearls are later harvested, the oyster has covered the nucleus with layers of nacre. Near-white Akoya cultured pearls are produced in Japan. In the warmer waters of the South Pacific, larger oysters produce white, "silver," or "golden" South Sea cultured pearls and Tahitian black cultured pearls. Freshwater pearls are cultured in mussels, mostly in China.

Cutting, setting, and valuing: The quality of pearls is judged both by their orient—the soft iridescent sheen caused by the refraction of light by the layers of nacre—and their luster. Fine pearls have no flaws or spots in the nacre, and exhibit an even, smooth texture. Other quality factors include size, roundness, color, and—for strands of pearls—how well they are matched. Black pearls are highly valued. Chinese freshwater pearls are abundantly available, and faceted and mosaic-inlaid pearls have now been introduced. Pearls can be dyed or irradiated to almost any color. Plastic and glass beads imitate pearls.

Refractive index:	1.530–1.685 (for aragonite)
Birefringence:	0.155 (for aragonite)
Dispersion:	0.017 (for aragonite)
Specific gravity:	2.60–2.78 (for natural pearls; cultured pearls may differ from this)
Hardness:	2.5-3.5
Cleavage:	none
Fracture:	uneven
Luster:	pearly
Notable locations:	Persian Gulf, India, Sri Lanka, Scotland, Germany, Philippines, Malaysia, Australia, China, Tahiti, Japan, Mexico, Panama, Venezuela
Color:	white to yellow to brown, gray to black, yellow to pink to purple-pink or lavender, all with purple-pink or blue-green orient

Organic Pearl

The gemstone gallery

The following pages contain a gallery of all the
gemstones featured in the Directory. This at-a-glance
guide allows you to see the gemstones in all their
variety and glory. Like the pages of this book, the
Gallery is organized by gemstone shape, or crystal
system. This means that you can see, for example,
all the cubic gems alongside each other. You can use
the gallery as a useful aid to identification, or simply
as an interesting pictorial reference.

Cubic

Diamond

Pyrope
Garnet

Spessartine
Garnet

Almandine
Garnet

Uvarovite
Garnet

Grossular
Garnet

Hessonite
Grossular Garnet

Tsavorite
Grossular Garnet

Andradite
Garnet

Pyrite

Sphalerite

Spinel

Cubic continued

Fluorite

Sodalite

Haüyne

Lazurite
Lapis Lazuli

Tetragonal

Scheelite

Cassiterite

Scapolite
Marialite–Meionite Series

Rutile

Zircon

Vesuvianite

Tetragonal continued

Tugtupite

Hexagonal

Emerald
Beryl

Aquamarine
Beryl

Heliodor
Beryl

Goshenite
Beryl

Morganite

Red Beryl

Apatite

Taaffeite

Benitoite

Trigonal

Rose Quartz

Rock Crystal Quartz

Amethyst Quartz

Citrine Quartz

Aventurine Quartz

Milky Quartz

Chatoyant Quartz

Quartz with Inclusions

Agate
Chalcedony

Fire Agate
Chalcedony

Onyx, Sard, and Sardonyx
Chalcedony

Chrysoprase
Chalcedony

Jasper
Chalcedony

Carnelian
Chalcedony

Bloodstone
Chalcedony

Gaspeite

Ruby
Corundum

Sapphire
Corundum

Padparadscha Sapphire
Corundum

Colorless Sapphire
Corundum

Green Sapphire
Corundum

Pink Sapphire
Corundum

Yellow Sapphire
Corundum

Eudialyte

Calcite

Phenakite

Dioptase

Dolomite

Smithsonite

Rhodochrosite

Rubellite
Elbaite or Liddicoatite Tourmaline

Indicolite
Elbaite or Liddicoatite Tourmaline

Dravite
Tourmaline

Achroite
Elbaite or Rossmanite Tourmaline

Watermelon Tourmaline
Elbaite or Liddicoatite

Schorl
Tourmaline

Trigonal continued

Paraíba Tourmaline
Elbaite

Orthorhombic

Aragonite

Barite

Celestine

Cerussite

Topaz

Chrysoberyl

Andalusite

Danburite

Enstatite

Orthorhombic continued

Sillimanite

Hypersthene

Iolite
Cordierite

Kornerupine

Peridot
Forsterite

Anglesite

Sinhalite

Hambergite

Prehnite

Zoisite
including Tanzanite

Staurolite

Dumortierite

The gemstone gallery

Monoclinic

Beryllonite

Brazilianite

Diopside

Meerschaum
Sepiolite

Spodumene

Epidote

Titanite
Sphene

Orthoclase

Moonstone
Orthoclase

Euclase

Jadeite
Jade

Nephrite
Jade

Malachite

Chrysocolla

Azurite

Serpentine

Phosphophyllite

Maw-Sit-Sit

Lazulite

Howlite

Gypsum

Datolite

Triclinic

Microcline

Albite

Oligoclase

Labradorite

Turquoise

Rhodonite

Amblygonite

Axinite Mineral Group

Kyanite

Amorphous

Opal

Obsidian

Moldavite

The gemstone gallery

Amorphous continued

Amber

Jet

Various

Ivory

Shell and Tortoise Shell

Coral

Organic

Pearl

Identifying and collecting minerals and gemstones

Knowing how to identify a gem is a basic skill for a collector in the field, but it is no less important for an amateur buyer of cut stones. Mineral specimens are often unlabeled, or labeled incorrectly. You should use your judgment, or that of a trusted expert, to check the identification of a mineral that you buy in a garage sale, from an antique shop, or even at a jewelry store.

You should make an assessment based on all the easily visible characteristics of a gem, such as color, shape, and habit. You may also want to examine your gem under a loupe, or even resort to microscopic analysis using the many hi-tech testing techniques that are now available.

Identifying minerals

Many minerals can be identified by close examination, particularly if the specimen is in the shape of a well-formed crystal. When trying to identify a crystal, consider its properties one by one. Working in a systematic way will allow you to eliminate many of the most common mineral species from consideration, and thus narrow the possibilities.

Color is an obvious way of telling one stone apart from another, and is the first thing that you should look at. Bear in mind that color is a less reliable indicator than it might first appear. Many stones come in a range of colors, and one mineral may have a color that is identical to that of another. A mineral's color may be due to one of the elements in its composition (in which case the gem is termed "ideochromatic") or it may be due to trace elements or inclusions (for which the term is "allochromatic"). Almost all specimens are stained orangy-brown on their surfaces when taken from the ground, and this can disguise the real color.

Next, consider the crystal's diaphaneity—that is, whether it is transparent, translucent, or opaque. Some minerals are always opaque or translucent. However, some normally transparent minerals can also be turned translucent or opaque by the presence of inclusions. Now look at its habit. Is the mineral

RIGHT *This crystal is forsterite, known in the gem trade as peridot.*

elongated, stubby, columnlike (prismatic), or pyramidal? Does it form an obvious cube or an octahedron (eight-sided shape)? If the material is aggregated, does it form round masses, like grapes (botryoidal), or is it granular? Remember that some crystals have more than one habit, which can make identification trickier. Now look for the flat bounding planes (crystal faces). Try to determine the angles at which the faces intersect, so that you can establish to which of the seven systems your mineral belongs.

Notice how the crystal faces reflect light. Is the luster shiny or dull? Consider whether there are any other qualities that could help with identification; for example, some crystals may have fine lines (striations) or "etch" features on the faces. Cleavage and fracture can be a useful indicators for identification. Cleavage is a clean, flat break, which may be parallel, diagonal, or perpendicular to a crystal face. It is often more lustrous than a crystal face and will show an impact point where the break started. As for fracture, look for a fresh nonplanar surface where the crystal has broken, to see what type of fracture it is displaying. Is it smooth with undulations or curves, as occurs when glass is broken (conchoidal)? Or is it jagged, splintery, or uneven?

Once you have finished your visual examination of the crystal, try to ascertain its hardness. A set of hardness points can be used to scratch the crystal. If you don't have such a set, you can use a piece of quartz (hardness 7) or a steel knife blade (hardness 5½) to help you. If a point or substance can make a scratch in your crystal, then the substance is harder than the crystal; using several points will help you to ascertain the hardness of your crystal. You should only scratch a rough stone, not a cut gem—and always choose an inconspicuous place.

BACKGROUND *Polymer impregnation may improve the luster of certain gemstones such as these turquoises, with their characteristic bright blue color.*

Identifying gems

Most cut and rough gem material does not have external crystal faces, so it is more difficult to identify from outward appearance than a well-formed crystal. It is therefore necessary to use the various tools of the gemologist's trade to examine its internal structure.

A good magnification system is essential. To see fine details, inclusions, and evidence of treatments, you need a handheld magnifier, or loupe. Diamond clarity grades are established at 10-times magnification, which is standard for loupes. A gemological microscope is more powerful, but a major investment.

You should begin any close examination of a gemstone by looking for fissures, patches of uneven color, or particles of foreign matter. Mineral grains show what other minerals were present where the gemstone formed, and this could help you to distinguish between a natural and a synthetic emerald, for example. The presence of gas bubbles in "negative crystals" (voids that are the same shape as the habit of the host crystal) indicate that a gem has probably not been heat treated.

There are other things that you can check for. Gems in which fractures have been filled can show a "flash effect" when you look at a fissure edge-on. Diffuse color zones may indicate extreme heat treatment, or the diffusion of other elements into the gem's surface. If back facets and facet reflections appear doubled, then that indicates that the gem is not isotropic and not glass.

Look at the gem between crossed polarized filters: Bright colors indicate birefringence, and patterns or bright local color can indicate strain within the structure of the gem. Photo-atlases of minerals and gems, and gemological websites are good places to compare any features you see.

Additional properties will have to be measured. Measuring specific gravity involves weighing the sample in air and suspended in water; to do this you will need a balance that can weigh a suspended object. The formula for specific gravity is: SG = (weight in air) / (weight in air − weight in water). To measure refractive indices and birefringence, you need a gemological refractometer. This contains a glass hemicylinder, onto which the gemstone is placed with a drop of refractive index fluid. Refractive indices are seen as shadow edges on an eyepiece; they may shift in position as the gemstone or a polarizer is rotated, so the maximum and minimum values of each edge you see should be noted. For the best results, a refractometer should be used in a dark room; the gemstone and hemicylinder must be carefully cleaned off afterwards.

Many gems have distinctive optical spectra which can be seen using a handheld spectroscope. Red spinel can be distinguished from ruby or red garnet and a common jade dye can be distinguished from natural green jadeite in this way. Ultraviolet lamps can be used to detect fluorescence, which can be an indication of the presence of fillers in a gem.

Taken together, the readings from these various instruments can be used to establish the mineral species of a gem. However, every property must correspond: The rare mineral taaffeite, for example, matches spinel in every respect except birefringence, and has been mistaken for it in the past. If in doubt, take your gem material to an expert jeweler or to the geology department of a university.

LEFT *A bright light can help you to see features in dark material, such as the gas bubbles in this jadeite bangle.*

BACKGROUND *Polarized light shows intergrown crystals. In this amethyst slice they appear as blue and yellow bands.*

Further testing

There is more to know about a gem than just its species. One might want to establish its exact variety; is it, for example, is it a ruby or a pink sapphire? Does the gemstone contain independent evidence as to where it was formed, or where it was found? Can one be certain that it is natural rather than synthetic? Questions such as these have a bearing on the importance and the value of a gem, and often the answers can only be provided by techniques that are beyond the means or the technical knowhow of most collectors.

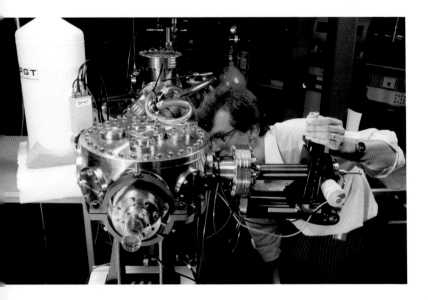

Among those techniques are the several varieties of spectrometry, which is measuring the ways that gemstones affect the various properties of light at the molecular level. UV-Visible-Near IR spectrometry, for example, looks at the wavelengths that a gemstone absorbs. This can be used to determine whether certain colors in diamonds are naturally occurring, or owe their color to treatment with ionizing radiation.

ABOVE *Proton microprobes detect small variations in chemical composition, and so can spot some subtle gem treatments.*

Infrared (IR) spectrometry is a different means of measuring light. It is sensitive to the presence of plastics and polymers in gemstones. This makes it very useful for establishing whether surface-reaching fissures in a gem have been filled with artificial materials. IR spectrometry also shows up the presence of water, which means that it can be used to distinguishing some synthetic gems from their natural counterparts, because the natural gems tend to contain tiny quantities of water, whereas these synthetics are anhydrous—that is, "dry."

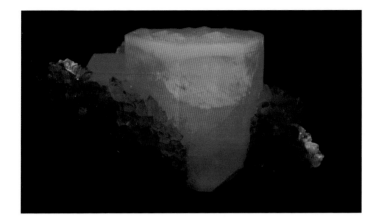

Raman spectrometry can target mineral inclusions in gemstones and identify them by the characteristic spectral patterns of the light that

ABOVE *A calcite crystal fluorescing to ultraviolet radiation. The orange glow indicates the presence of manganese.*

they emit. Inclusions can serve to verify that a gemstone is natural rather than synthetic; more than that, they can act like a geographical fingerprint, pinpointing the location where the gemstone was mined.

X-ray fluorescence (XRF) is a technique that exploits a different part of the invisible spectrum. It can be used to identify the elements that are present in a gem and, under the right circumstances, to measure the exact quantities of those elements and so determine the gem's mineral formula. The presence or absence of certain elements is yet another way of determining whether a gem is synthetic, or if it has undergone a treatment. X-raying can highlight the internal structure of pearls, for example, and so distinguish natural pearls from cultured ones. Some pearls emit luminescence when subjected to X-rays, which can be used to distinguish freshwater specimens from saltwater ones.

Then there is photoluminescence testing, practically the only way to detect high-pressure high-temperature (HPHT), a treatment that can render brown diamonds colorless. Using laser-induced breakdown spectroscopy (LIBS) or an ion microprobe are ways to detect a sapphire that has been turned from pink to orange by beryllium diffusion. All these methods of testing add up to a fine mineralogical armory, a battery of sophisticated technology that can be found only in a gem-testing laboratory.

BACKGROUND *Pearls and other gems can be X-rayed using techniques similar to those used by dentists to X-ray teeth.*

Gemstone evaluation

It takes years of experience to know how to value gemstones; appraisers are highly skilled professionals. You might require an appraisal for a variety of purposes such as insurance replacement or tax-deductible donations. However, the basis for an appraisal is always the "fair market value," that is, the price that a willing buyer will pay, and the price a willing seller will accept. For rare and high-value goods, an open auction is the only way to determine the fair market value. For commercially available goods, the fair market value can be determined by comparing the item with similar ones that are on the market.

The first step in evaluating a gem is to determine its identity: its species and variety, how it was formed (for example, whether in nature or in a laboratory), where it was first found, and if its provenance is well documented or corroborated by internal features. It is also important to know whether the gem has been treated in any way.

Once the gemstone's identity has been ascertained, the next question for the appraiser is to establish its quality. The method used to do this is usually summed up by the term "the four Cs." These are color, clarity, cut, and carat weight. In general, bright colors that are typical of the stone in question are worth the most, and brownish and grayish stones are worth less.

BELOW *A jeweler sorting melee (small diamonds). He is using a gauge to determine the precise size of the gems.*

Transparent gems are more valuable when they have no inclusions. Open fissures that can break the stone into pieces are particularly undesirable.

ABOVE *An exceptional round brilliant diamond. Well-cut gems such as this command a premium in the marketplace.*

The cut of a gem means, first and foremost, the stone's shape, the style into which it has been fashioned. The term also includes the quality of the work, which is judged by how well the stone returns light, its symmetry, whether the faceting looks graceful or clumsy, and whether or not it has excess weight for its style. Carat weight is naturally a fundamental factor in judging its worth. However, it does not follow that a two-carat gem will cost twice as much as two equivalent one-carat gems, since large gems may be much rarer than smaller ones and so more valuable. The cost-to-weight equation will vary from one gemstone to another, depending on how often large gems are found.

Additional factors that can increase the value of a gem include the presence of phenomena such as a cat's eye (chatoyancy) or star (asterism). Other phenomena that make a gem more valuable are change of color, in which a gem appears a different color when viewed under different types of light; and adularescence, in which a flash of white or colored light is seen as the gem is moved. An interesting inclusion, a prestigious locality of origin, or an interesting history can also affect value.

Lately, an important concern for consumers has been the ethical sourcing of gems. Buyers are increasingly looking for "green" gems, that is, those that have been mined without causing environmental damage, and those that help support local and third-world communities. The Kimberley Process was set up to prevent bloody regimes profiting from diamond smuggling (see page 9), and dealers in colored stones are working to set up a system of fair trade imports, guaranteeing that miners and their communities share in the profits from gem sales.

RIGHT *Gold flakes, such as these, can be newly mined, or they can be sourced from recycling operations.*

Mineral evaluation and storing

Mineral specimens are evaluated in much the same way as gems, but some additional conditions apply. Once a mineral has been identified, the first consideration is to establish the quality of the specimens. Some minerals, such as quartz, are often found in sharp crystalline form, and so are less valuable than crystals of, say, turquoise, which are rare.

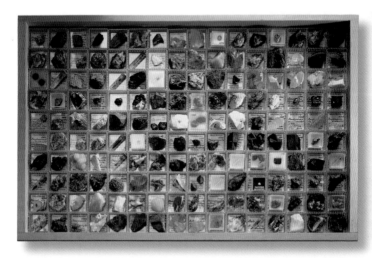

The second consideration is condition. Complete undamaged crystals are generally worth much more than those crystals that are

ABOVE *In a well-kept mineral collection, such as this one, every specimen is identified and stored safely.*

"bruised" on the showiest side. Sometimes mineral specimens are "oiled" (coated or soaked in mineral oil) and this can disguise any parts that are damaged, as well as making crystal faces more lustrous. In general, soft and delicate minerals are at a premium, because undamaged examples are much harder to come by. Locality is another factor that affects the value of mineral specimens. Where is the mineral from? Is the locality already famous (Bisbee, Arizona, for example, is known for malachite), or does this specimen hail from a previously unknown source? Is this mineral an exceptionally good specimen for its locality?

Just as important is the aesthetic appeal of the specimen: There is an element of art appreciation in the pricing of minerals. Does the specimen look attractive from all sides, or is there (at least) one good side? Is the size of a crystal of interest large compared to its matrix, that is, the rock on which or in which the crystal grew? Can the mineral specimen stand up by itself, thereby making it a better display item? Does it have a resemblance to an interesting object or figure—for example, a seahorse, landscape, or dragon? The matrix should

ABOVE *Minerals are often displayed with their species and locality information. These are in a well-lit, dust-free cabinet.*

not outshine or compete with the crystal, but there are aspects of the matrix that may serve to increase the value of the piece of the whole. For example, what other minerals are present in the matrix? Are they also well crystallized? What is their condition? Are any of these minerals rare, or otherwise remarkable? The final consideration is the history of the piece. Did it come from a collection of historic importance? Does it come with any old labels, especially famous ones? Was it part of a historic find? If so, then the worth of the piece may exceed its purely gemological value.

BUILDING A COLLECTION

A collection is more than an accumulation of minerals, it also reflects the interests of the collector. Some collectors like to focus on particular groups of minerals—such as gemstones or copper minerals—or to collect only specimens of particular sizes such as "thumbnails," those that fit in a 1-in (2.5-cm) cube.

To keep its value, a collection needs to be stored safely. Some minerals decompose, and some (such as elemental sulfur) cause other specimens to tarnish. Some are light sensitive, and many react with humidity. Fumes given off by wood and composite materials can damage specimens or their labels. In a well-housed collection, each specimen is accompanied by its label, in an individual box in a cabinet drawer, or in a closed display case.

A mineral specimen loses much of its value when it loses historic information, especially the details of where it was found. In the past, specimens were given numbers which were painted or glued on the mineral, and the information listed in bound-book or card catalogs. Today, catalog information is easily stored on computer, but a label should still accompany the specimen, stating what mineral or minerals are present and where it or they were found.

Gemstones by color

Gemstones by color

Bloodstone (Chalcedony)
116–117
Calcite 136–137
Celestine 166–167
Cerussite 168–169
Chatoyant Quartz 100–101
Chrysocolla 230–231
Coral 280–281
Diamond 24–25
Diopside 208–209
Dumortierite 202–203
Euclase 222–223
Fluorite 48–49
Haüyne 52–53
Indicolite (Tourmaline)
150–151
Iolite (Cordierite) 184–185
Jasper (Chalcedony)
112–113
Kyanite 264–265
Lazulite 238–239
Lazurite (Lapis Lazuli) 54–55
Microcline 248–249
Opal 266–267
Paraíba Tourmaline
160–161
Phosphophyllite 236–237
Sapphire (Corundum)
122–123
Scapolite 60–61
Serpentine 234–235
Sillimanite 180–181
Smithsonite 144–145
Sodalite 50–51
Spinel 46–47
Taaffeite 84–85
Tanzanite (Zoisite) 198–199
Topaz 170–171
Tugtupite 68–69
Turquoise 256–257
Vesuvianite 66–67
Zircon 64–65

Violet and Purple

Agate (Chalcedony)
104–105
Almandine 30–31
Amethyst (Quartz) 92–93
Andalusite 174–175
Apatite 82–83

Axinite 262–263
Benitoite 86–87
Calcite 136–137
Cassiterite 58–59
Coral 280–281
Diamond 24–25
Diopside 208–209
Dumortierite 202–203
Fluorite 48–49
Iolite (Cordierite) 184–185
Jadeite 224–225
Paraíba Tourmaline
160–161
Pearl 282–283
Rubellite (Tourmaline)
148–149
Sapphire (Corundum)
122–123
Scapolite 60–61
Shell 278–279
Spinel 46–47
Spodumene 212–213
Taaffeite 84–85
Tanzanite (Zoisite) 198–199
Vesuvianite 66–67

Pink

Amblygonite 260–261
Andalusite 174–175
Apatite 82–83
Calcite 136–137
Coral 280–281
Danburite 176–177
Diamond 24–25
Dolomite 142–143
Dumortierite 202–203
Fluorite 48–49
Grossular 34–35
Gypsum 244–245
Haüyne 52–53
Jasper (Chalcedony)
112–113
Microcline 248–249
Moonstone (Orthoclase)
220–221
Morganite (Beryl) 78–79
Opal 266–267
Pearl 282–283
Phenakite 138–139
Pyrope 26–27

Rhodochrosite 146–147
Rhodonite 258–259
Rose Quartz 88–89
Rubellite (Tourmaline)
148–149
Sapphire (Corundum)
122–125, 130–131
Scapolite 60–61
Shell 278–279
Sodalite 50–51
Smithsonite 144–145
Spinel 46–47
Spodumene 212–213
Taaffeite 84–85
Topaz 170–171
Tugtupite 68–69
Watermelon Tourmaline
156–157
Zoisite 198–199

Red

Agate (Chalcedony)
104–105
Almandine 30–31
Amber 272–273
Andradite 40–41
Aragonite 162–163
Barite 164–165
Calcite 136–137
Carnelian (Chalcedony)
114–115
Cassiterite 58–59
Celestine 166–167
Coral 280–281
Datolite 246–247
Diamond 24–25
Eudialyte 134–135
Fire Agate (Chalcedony)
106–107
Grossular 34–37
Gypsum 244–245
Hessonite (Grossular)
36–37
Iolite (Cordierite) 184–185
Jadeite 224–225
Jasper (Chalcedony)
112–113
Microcline 248–249
Opal 266–267
Pyrope 26–27

Resources

GEMOLOGY

P.G. Read and R. Webster, **Gems, 5th Edition** (1995), Butterworth-Heinemann, 1072 pages.
This is the definitive reference on common and uncommon gems, but does not include more recent finds.

E.J. Gübelin and J.I. Koivula, **Photoatlas of Inclusions in Gemstones**, Vol. 1 (1986), ABC Press, Zurich, 532 pages.
Beautiful and exemplary images through the microscope of inclusions in many species of gems.

E.J. Gübelin and J.I. Koivula, **Photoatlas of Inclusions in Gemstones**, Vol. 2 (2005), Opinio Verlag, Basel, 829 pages.
Continues the library of gem inclusions seen through the microscope, with new information after 1986. (A third volume is also in the works.)

J.I. Koivula, **The MicroWorld of Diamonds** (2000), Gemworld International, 157 pages.
Images of diamonds through the microscope.

C.S. Hurlbut Jr. and R.C. Kammerling, **Gemology** (1991), Wiley-Interscience, 352 pages.
Basic gemology, teaching how to measure properties and introducing many common gem materials.

R.T. Liddicoat Jr., **Handbook of Gem Identification**, 12th Edition (1993), Gemological Institute of America, 450 pages.
Basic gemological reference, the standard as used in Gemological Institute of America courses.

Peer-reviewed gemological journals, including **Gems & Gemology, The Journal of Gemology**, and others.

The jewelry trade press, including **Jeweler's Circular-Keystone (JCK), Modern Jeweler, Professional Jeweler, National Jeweler**, and many others.
See especially **Modern Jeweler's Gem Portrait** series, http://www.modernjeweler.com/online/gemProfile.jsp

The Gemological Association and Gem Testing Laboratory of Great Britain, http://www.gem-a.info/
The first significant gemological school.

The Gemological Institute of America, http://www.gia.edu
An all-purpose gemological source of information, including a school, library, laboratory, instrument source, journal, and active alumni association.

The American Gem Society, http://www.americangemsociety.org/
Group promoting jeweler ethics and continuous education, plus a diamond grading laboratory.

The American Gem Trading Association, http://www.agta.org/
A colored stone trade organization with a colored stone identification laboratory.

Other useful websites include:

http://gemologyproject.com

www.heartofstonestudio.com:
A jeweler's website, selling designer cabochons and faceted stones as well as offering free bench tips on metalsmithing and glass fusing.

MINERALOGY

R.V. Gaines et al., **Dana's New Mineralogy: The System of Mineralogy of James Dwight Dana and Edward Salisbury Dana** [Eighth Edition] (1997), John Wiley & Sons, 1819 pages.
Terse descriptions of all (then) known minerals, organized by chemistry and structural backbone.

C. Klein and B. Dutrow, **Manual of Mineral Science** [23rd edition of Dana's Manual of Mineralogy] (2007), John Wiley & Sons, 704 pages.
Good description of mineralogy and how to determine mineral properties, with descriptions of many common minerals.

R. S. Mitchell, **Mineral Names: What Do They Mean?** (1979), Van Nostrand Rheinhold, 229 pages.
Useful insights into mineral names.

W.L. Roberts, G.R. Rapp Jr., and J. Weber, **Encyclopedia of Minerals** (1974), Van Nostrand Reinhold, 693 pages.
This book has short descriptions of all (then) known minerals, and several inset pages with pictures of microscopic crystals (a second edition also exists, but has different photos).

The Photo-Atlas of Minerals (version 2.0), DVD produced by the Gem & Mineral Council, Natural History Museum of Los Angeles, http://www.nhm.org/pam
Extensive (as of 2007) descriptions of minerals and their properties, with copious images for most.

Peer-reviewed journals for amateurs, such as **The Mineralogical Record, Rocks & Minerals,** and **Lapis**.

To find a local mineral club, contact one of the following.
USA: **The American Federation of Mineral Societies,** http://www.amfed.org

Canada Gem & Mineral Federation of Canada, http://www.gmfc.ca
UK The Russell Society, http://www.russellsoc.org/

Professional mineral societies:

Mineralogical Society of Great Britain and Ireland, http://www.minersoc.org/
Mineralogical Society of America, http://www.minsocam.org/
Mineralogical Association of Canada, http://www.mineralogicalassociation.ca/

Other useful websites include:

http://www.mindat.org/ and http://www.webmineral.com/
for general mineral data,
and http://rruff.info/
for chemical and spectral information; this website provides information to help identify a mineral specimen.

Appraisal references:

The American Society of Appraisers (ASA), http://www.appraisers.org
The International Society of Appraisers (ISA) http://isa-appraisers.org
The National Association of Jewelry Appraisers, http://www.NAJAappraisers.com
The Canadian Jewellers Institute http://www.canadianjewellers.com/html/aapmemberlist.htm

Mary L. Johnson:
For more information on identifying gems and on Dr. Johnson's scientific consulting firm, see
http://www.maryjohnsonconsulting.com/

Index

Picture Credits